Good wood guide

Proceeds from sales will contribute to the Global Trees Campaign of Fauna & Flora International and the ongoing work of Friends of the Earth.

Written by Georgina Magin on behalf of Fauna & Flora International
and Friends of the Earth

Edited by Lesley Smeardon
Design by Sarah Denney and Cottier & Sidaway Design Partnership

Acknowledgements
Thanks to the following for their invaluable help and support in writing
this book: Tiffany Aylett, Robert Garner, Paul Jepson, Thorton Kay,
Hazel Matravers, Ed Matthew, Sara Oldfield, Matt Phillips and Jamison Suter.

Supported by Fauna & Flora International through Fenside Waste Management Ltd
and the Rufford Foundation.

Reclaimed wood information supplied by Salvo.

ISBN 1 85750 342 2

Friends of the Earth
26-28 Underwood St
London N1 7JQ

Fauna & Flora International
Great Eastern House
Tenison Road
Cambridge CB1 2TT

Printed on paper made from 100 per cent post-consumer waste.

Contents

Introduction

Wood is an essential commodity for modern day life, found in a large variety of products including window frames, doors, furniture, tools and fencing. Our appetite for this material is huge. Globally, demand for wood is at an all time high, with the UK one of the largest per capita users in the world.

Growing pressure from a range of sources means that an area of forest the size of England is lost every year.

While wood is in principle a natural, renewable material, with advantages over environmentally-costly alternatives, such as steel or PVC, it is currently being extracted and used in an unsustainable way. Growing pressure from a range of sources means that an area of forest the size of England is lost every year. Corruption and illegal logging are rife in many countries and over 1,000 tree species are globally threatened with extinction because of logging. Many forest-dwelling animals and plants are perilously close to disappearing, and the livelihoods of some of the world's poorest people who depend directly on the forests are in serious jeopardy.

To add to the problem, we use wood very wastefully (during felling, processing and disposal) meaning more trees have to be felled to satisfy our needs. As the demand for wood products continues to grow, loggers are moving in to the last remote forests of the world.

The issues involved in forest loss are complex. There are no easy solutions, but as major consumers of wood products, we share a responsibility for the problems and have a significant role to play in resolving them. This guide is about how we, individual and professional timber users, can use our power as consumers to contribute to a better future for the world's forests. It is about providing practical information to allow us all to make informed choices about the timber products we buy and use.

By taking measures to minimise waste, we can help to manage the demand for wood products and ease the pressure on forests and tree species. Re-using old wood rather than throwing it away, for example, ensures we don't waste valuable timber resources. We must also ensure that the new products we buy are from well-managed forests. Thanks to the development of a reliable forest certification and labelling scheme, the Forest Stewardship Council (FSC), this is now possible. Choosing FSC labelled products sends a strong message that consumers do not want wood products that contribute to forest destruction and creates a powerful incentive to producers to manage forests sustainably.

Although this guide focuses on timber/wood, many of the same principles apply to buying paper.

Good wood guide checklist

The following advice has been put together to help you make the very best environmental choice when using wood. The checklist is presented in order, starting with the best environmental choice (step 1).

Step 1

Repair, restore or adapt an existing item

The best environmental choice is to repair, restore or adapt a product you already have. You may need professional help to do the work, but it could still work out cheaper than a brand new item and it's far better for the world's forests. *See Chapter 2 for more information on re-using your old timber and other ways to reduce your wood waste.*

Step 2

Buy a second-hand item or one made from recycled, reclaimed or waste timber

Using reclaimed/recycled or waste timber or buying second hand is a better environmental choice than buying new. *See Chapter 2 for tips on buying reclaimed timber and ways to reduce your wood waste. For a list of dealers supplying reclaimed timber see page 66.*

Step 3

The FSC is the only certification scheme recommended by Friends of the Earth and Fauna & Flora International.

Buy timber products produced locally that are FSC certified

If you are buying new, choose wood that comes from a local forest, certified by the Forest Stewardship Council (FSC). All FSC certified wood carries the FSC logo. Buying a locally-produced product means less fossil fuel is used for its transport. *See Chapter 4 for more information on the Forest Stewardship Council and certification schemes.*

Step 4

Buy FSC certified products from farther afield

If there is no timber available from a local FSC certified forest, opt for FSC products from farther afield. *See Chapter 4 for more information on certification.*

Note:

If you need to use wood with very specific properties for a specialised end use, you may not be able to find a suitable timber that is FSC certified. Without FSC certification, there is no guarantee that what you buy will have come from a well-managed forest. *Chapters 5 and 6 provide advice and information to help you make the best decision if you are in this difficult position.*

What to consider when buying new timber

Suitability

Make sure you select a timber product that has properties suitable for the function it will perform. If you don't, it may mean you will need to replace the timber after a short time, at a high cost to you and the environment.

Appearance

Don't buy endangered wood just to get the appearance you want. Most timber can be effectively stained to achieve a desired look.

Alternatives

Avoid using alternative materials, such as PVC, aluminium or steel, which have higher environmental costs than well-sourced timber (although alternatives made from waste or residues, such as strawboard or flaxboard, are a good environmental option). *See Chapter 3 for more information on timber products and alternatives.*

A note about paper

Although this guide focuses on timber and timber products, the same principles of waste reduction, recycling and sound sourcing apply to paper too. Minimising paper consumption by efficient use, and avoiding over-packaged items is the number one priority. Re-using envelopes, wrapping and writing paper is the next thing to think about. When a paper product no longer has a use, it should be recycled.

When buying paper, products made from 100 per cent recycled post-consumer waste are the best environmental option; these are now widely available. If for any reason you cannot buy recycled paper, FSC certification also applies to paper products. Choosing paper with the FSC logo will ensure the forests providing it have been well-managed.

Chapter 1 A global forest crisis

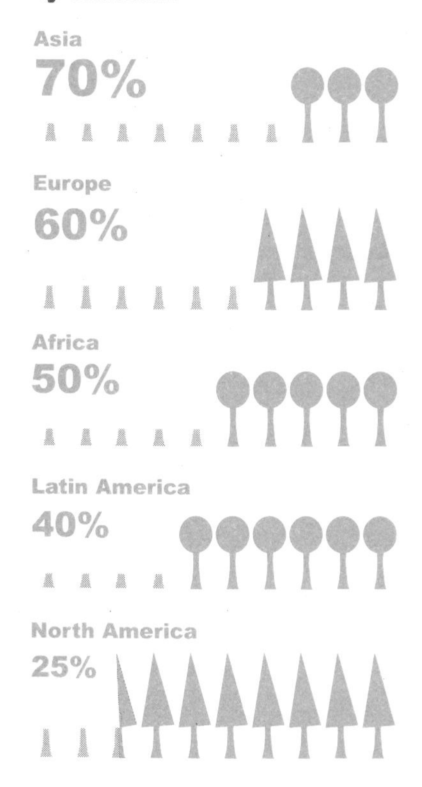

Forest loss continues at an alarming rate: an area the size of England was lost every year during the 1990s, mostly in developing countries.

What's happening to the world's forests?

The world's forests are in crisis. Globally, deforestation has been extensive and forest cover is now reduced to almost half its original extent. While some of this loss has occurred in historical times, a large proportion has disappeared within the past three decades. What is left is now highly fragmented; the World Resources Institute estimates that just 22 per cent of the Earth's original forest remains in large, relatively intact ecosystems (known as frontier forests). Over three-quarters of these frontier forests are found in three large blocks, one in Canada and Alaska, one stretching across Russia, and one covering the Amazon Basin of South America.

Despite global attention to the crisis, forest loss continues at an alarming rate: an area the size of England was lost every year during the 1990s, mostly in developing countries (14.6 million ha lost a year). As well as the reduction in forest area, there is also a loss of forest quality in many regions, with natural forests being turned into degraded forests.

The loss and degradation of forests have huge significance for environmental stability, global climate, biodiversity, and the welfare and future of some 350 million of the world's poorest people, who depend directly on the forests for their livelihoods. Many species of plants and animals are now threatened with extinction: the world is perilously close to losing the orangutan, Sumatran rhino, mountain gorilla and many hundreds of lesser-known plants and animals. It is estimated that 30,000 species may go extinct each year in tropical forests alone. In addition, over 8,000 tree species are globally threatened, 1,000 of them because of logging. These include timbers commonly used in the UK, such as meranti, sapele, utile, Brazilian and African mahogany.

Why is this happening?

Land clearance for subsistence or commercial agriculture is often blamed as the chief cause of deforestation and it is a very significant factor in many regions. But the timber industry is also a major cause of forest loss and degradation. It is estimated, for example, that unsustainable logging for wood products is responsible for approximately one-third of total global deforestation to date, and commercial logging has been identified as the most important threat to the world's remaining frontier forests.

Logging not only destroys or damages the forest directly, it can also act as a catalyst for other changes. Roads built to extract timber allow settlers into

It is estimated that unsustainable logging for wood products is responsible for approximately one-third of total global deforestation. Commercial logging has been identified as the most important threat to the world's remaining frontier forests.

previously inaccessible areas, leading to further damage or deforestation for agriculture.

A whole host of issues surrounds the global timber industry. Several key factors are external to the forest sector, for example, national debt, globalisation, national governance and the international trade regime. Others relate to the performance of the timber trade itself. While timber sales could, in theory, provide valuable income for poor countries rich in forest resources, many nations under-price their wood and the profit largely accrues to the (often foreign) logging companies. The objective of the loggers is frequently to maximise short-term profit from timber sales with little or no thought for the longer-term future of the forest or the people that live there.

The issues surrounding the timber industry vary according to region. In some areas (eg much of Europe), forest has been destroyed or degraded over many centuries, and almost all timber now comes from intensively managed forests or plantations. The main problem in these areas is the quality of these man-made habitats. In other regions (eg much of the tropics, North America and Russia), logging is largely in natural forest (some completely undisturbed, some previously harvested), and the multiple values of the forest are being destroyed or degraded by current logging practices.

Corruption and illegal logging

Corruption and illegal logging have become widespread in many countries. In some regions, forests are used as a way of securing political power and patronage, with concessions being handed out to the rich or political elite with no consideration for how the forests will be managed. Corrupt and illegal practices occur on every level, from the loggers to the forest officials supposed to regulate them, to senior politicians, businessmen and army generals. Illegal logging destroys the forest and deprives countries and communities of the much-needed income that could be derived from sustainable timber harvesting.

Illegal logging far outweighs legal activities in certain areas. In the Brazilian Amazon for example, a staggering 80 per cent of timber harvested is estimated to be illegal; in Indonesia it is 70 per cent. But the problem is not limited to the tropics: at least 20 per cent of timber logged in Russia violates current legislation, and 16 random audits of forest operations in British Colombia, Canada, found 19 cases of non-compliance with forest laws.

Logging profits used to support rebels in Sierra Leone

Reports from the international organisation Global Witness suggest that profits from rapid and unsustainable logging by the corrupt government in Liberia are being used to support the rebel movement in neighbouring Sierra Leone. Liberia contains some of the last untouched areas of forest in West Africa.

Logging and human rights abuses

A large proportion of forest worldwide is claimed by indigenous people under traditional land-use rights, which although recognised in international conventions are frequently not acknowledged by national governments. Forest allocation to commercial interests, such as logging companies, without indigenous peoples' consent is a frequent abuse of indigenous rights. The conflict that follows has often resulted in arrest, injury and even death.

Protesting against forest allocation

In Sarawak, Malaysia, the indigenous Penan people have undertaken extensive protests and blockades against the allocation of the forests where they live to logging companies. The protests have frequently been met with violence and imprisonment. In Canada, protests over logging in British Colombia's forests have resulted in excessive jail sentences, while timber companies in North America have begun to use law suits against protesters to prevent them from speaking out.

Bushmeat and logging

Another growing concern is the over-hunting of wildlife in areas opened up for logging. Forest-dwelling communities have traditionally hunted wild animals, which provide them with an important source of protein. However, as logging roads and motorised transport have improved access into remote forest areas, this traditional, small-scale activity has been replaced by large-scale commercial hunting and trade to supply the growing towns and cities, as well as to feed the new logging communities. Hunters frequently use logging vehicles as transport into the forest and for carrying the meat to the towns.

With the spread of commercial logging into more and more forest regions, over-hunting and the depletion of animal populations is now a very serious threat in many areas. The hunting of great apes (eg gorilla, chimpanzee) in central and west Africa is particularly grave.

Future prospects

There have been many international efforts to improve the situation of the world's forests over the past decades, and these are continuing (*see Appendix*). Most have been ineffectual and some have actually been blamed for worsening the problems. A number of countries have introduced national reforms and initiatives and they should be commended for these efforts, but the situation in many countries remains dire.

With global demand for wood at an all time high and still growing (predicted to increase by 26 per cent between 1996 and 2010), timber companies are now moving into the last remote forest areas of the world. Several large Malaysian companies, for example, having depleted timber supplies in their own country are securing concessions in the so-far less exploited primary forests of the Amazon Basin, the Congo Basin and the Russian Far East, causing great concern for the future of these last untouched areas.

Poaching and logging in Cameroon

In south-east Cameroon, 85 per cent of the meat taken by poachers is transported out of the forest on logging trucks, and 75 per cent of poachers are ex-loggers.

How is the UK involved?

The UK is one of the highest users of industrial wood (not counting that used for subsistence uses and firewood) in the world. In 1999, we consumed 46.7 million m^3 of wood (including that used for paper), enough to fill double-decker buses queueing nose-to-tail from London to Newfoundland. But UK production of timber is very low, and approximately 85 per cent of the wood we use is imported. The UK is thought to be the number one importer of illegal tropical timber in the European Union – an estimated 60 per cent of all tropical timber imports in the UK may be from illegal sources (worth approximately £140 million a year). We in the UK have a prime responsibility to limit our impact on the world's forests by using timber and paper more wisely.

Wood waste

At every stage of timber use, wastage is enormous. At harvesting, up to 45 per cent of the wood in the cut tree can be wasted. At the sawmill, normally only a maximum of 50 per cent of the main product (sawn timber) is recovered, although co-products, such as offcuts and sawdust, are often used for the wood panel industries in Northern countries at least. At secondary processing, up to 50 per cent of a piece of sawn timber may be discarded in the production of furniture or joinery. Ultimately, from one felled tree, just 14 per cent may actually be used in a piece of furniture.

In one selectively logged forest in French Guiana, it was estimated that for every tree extracted an average of 57 trees were killed.

Amount of wood wasted at each stage of timber processing

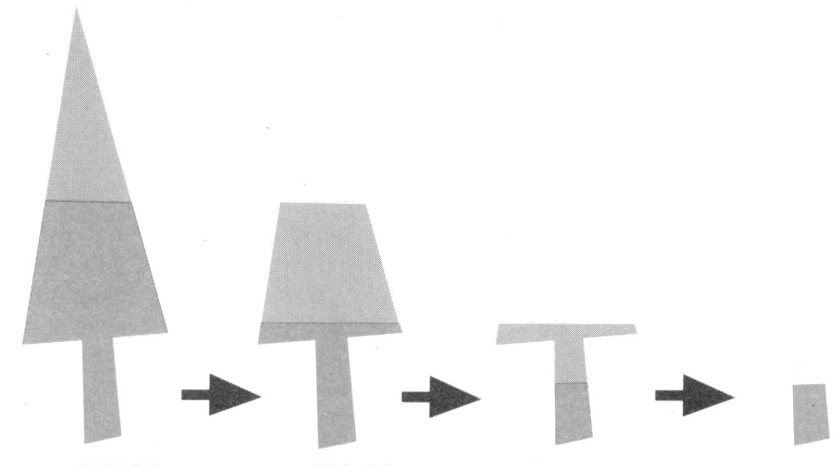

Only **55%** of the wood of a cut tree may be harvested.

Just **50%** of this wood is made into sawn timber.

Only **50%** of a piece of sawn timber may be used in making furniture.

In total, just **14%** of a tree may be used in the major wood products.

Finally, unwanted timber from old products and buildings is often thrown away when it could be saved and used again. It is estimated in the UK that at least 750,000 tonnes a year of reclaimable timber is landfilled or burnt from the demolition of old buildings alone.

What can we do to help?

As major consumers of forest products, we in the UK are part of the problem facing the world's forests. But we can also be part of the solution. Everyone can contribute to improving the sustainability of wood use in the UK and to bringing about change in the way the world's forests are managed.

As major consumers of forest products, we in the UK are part of the problem facing the world's forests. But we can also be part of the solution.

Reduce waste to manage demand

The huge demand for wood and wood products is a key factor that drives the timber industry. We in the UK must take responsibility for controlling and managing the amount of wood we use. Reducing waste and improving efficiency in the use of timber and paper products are key to moving towards more sustainable wood use – *see Chapter 2 for how you can help do this.*

Insist timber products come from well-managed forests
In a highly competitive timber market, consumer preference for products from well-managed forests can provide a powerful incentive for producers to improve forest management. The development of independent third party forest certification and labelling schemes gives consumers unprecedented power to influence the way forests are managed, by enabling people to "put their money where their mouth is".

Forest certification schemes are described in detail in Chapter 3. Although several such schemes have been developed, the only one that is currently recommended as giving any real guarantee of good forest management is the Forest Stewardship Council (FSC). By choosing products that carry the FSC logo, you can reward good practice, reject unsustainably harvested timber and demonstrate your concern over the future of forests to the timber industry and governments worldwide.

While FSC certification and the range of labelled products available is growing rapidly, there may still be occasions when it is not possible to locate a suitable certified timber, and concerned timber buyers will be faced with difficult choices about the use of uncertified wood. Using the information about timber types, origins and conservation status in Chapters 5 and 6 will help you to make the best environmental choice and minimise any negative impact on forests and endangered trees.

Support NGOs working on forests
Non-government organisations (NGOs), including Fauna & Flora International and Friends of the Earth, are crucial to sounding the alarm about the problems of forest loss and degradation, and in helping to find solutions. NGOs rely on the support of the public, and governments and industry pay attention when issues are seen to generate widespread popular concern. Joining and getting involved with NGOs working on forest issues is a key way people can help effect change.

For more information about the work of Friends of the Earth and Fauna & Flora International see pages 80-81.

Chapter 2 Cutting timber waste

The pressure on forests and tree species could be significantly eased if timber were used less wastefully. From forester to manufacturer, architect or builder to consumer, we can all use timber more efficiently.

1 Don't make unnecessary purchases

Think carefully about whether you really need a product, or whether an existing item could be repaired or restored instead of buying new.

2 Minimise waste during use

To reduce waste levels significantly when using wood, consider the following key issues.

Design
A carefully designed building or item can both reduce the amount of timber needed to produce the structure and the waste generated during the manufacturing or construction process.

Check out the professionals
If you are having work done for you, ensure that the professionals you use (eg architect, builder, cabinet maker) are waste conscious, making every effort to minimise waste at all stages.

Sourcing
Specifying and sourcing the correct dimension and grade of timber for a job is vital. A lot of timber is wasted because the raw material is bought in a standard size that does not match the requirements, or is of the wrong grade. Either consider the dimensions and grades available before you design, or make an effort to source the correct size and type.

Durability
The repair and replacement of damaged or decayed timber accounts for a significant proportion of wood used; making things to last is key to reducing timber waste. If the item will be subject to heavy exposure and wear, don't choose a product or timber type with low durability that will have to be replaced within a short time period, even if it appears to have a better environmental profile. In the long term, it may be far worse for the environment.

Storage and transport

Storing and transporting timber carefully minimises damage and therefore waste. Surplus timber from one job can be kept for use on another job or in supporting functions.

3 Re-use your old timber

Re-use your old timber. Think whether you can pass it on to family, friends, neighbours or a local school or community group.

Don't send old timber to landfill

Timber is estimated to make up 7-10 per cent of material taken to public waste sites (civic amenity sites). However, much of it may still have a use.

If you need to get rid of a timber item from your house or garden, try not to send anything to landfill. Think whether you can pass it on to family, friends, neighbours or a local school or community group. Good quality timber offcuts of a reasonable size from a DIY or home improvement project, for example, may be valued by a youth or school woodwork group.

Furniture

There is an extensive network of over 300 furniture recycling projects around the UK that take re-usable items and pass them on to low-income families. Some of these projects will also do simple repairs on slightly damaged items. The schemes are co-ordinated by an organisation called SOFA; to find your local scheme consult SOFA's website on www.btinternet.com/~frn/FRN or telephone 01924 375252. Some charity shops also take good quality second-hand furniture.

Timber joinery and fitments

Good quality timber items from around your home, such as doors, fireplaces and kitchen units, might be worth selling, especially period items from Victorian times. You could try contacting a reclaimed yard (*see listings in Chapter 7*), who may be interested in buying a really good item. Alternatively you could try selling it yourself via an advert in your local shop, paper, or on Salvo's DIY Wants and Offers web page (www.salvo.co.uk).

Timber recycling at waste sites

A few local authorities re-use or recycle timber at household waste sites (civic amenity sites). Contact Fauna & Flora International to find out if yours does (tel: 01223 571000).

It is estimated that over 3,000 tonnes of re-usable wood is thrown away or burnt from the demolition of old buildings in the UK every working day.

4 Choose reclaimed timber over new material

A lot of timber from old buildings is thrown away when it could be re-used. It is estimated that over 3,000 tonnes of re-usable wood is thrown away or burnt from the demolition of old buildings alone in the UK every working day – an amount that could build around 375 average new houses. About 10 per cent of the timber thrown away is estimated to be tropical hardwood, and a lot of it is very good quality, coming from old, slow-growing forests.

To reduce pressure on the world's forests, the best environmental choice when choosing wood is to use reclaimed timber. Furniture, fitted kitchens and other items made from reclaimed timber (most commonly pine but some other timbers too) are fairly widely available. Many bespoke furniture makers also regularly use reclaimed pine.

There is also a thriving trade in reclaimed building materials, involving approximately 2,500 businesses throughout the UK. The majority of materials travel very small distances from the site of disposal to a salvage yard, meaning the environmental costs of transport are also relatively low. A variety of timber items are commonly found at reclaimed yards, including beams, doors, flooring, sawn timber, and more elaborately worked items. If you are planning home renovations or extensions, try to use at least some reclaimed timber or timber items if you can – *see listings in Chapter 7*.

Commonly available reclaimed items

Reclaimed beams, which may be softwood, native hardwood (mainly oak) or tropical hardwood, are popular items, with annual sales in the UK totalling £42 million. A quarter of all reclaimed oak beams sold in the UK are now imported from abroad, mainly from France. Currently, one UK business provides stress-graded reclaimed timber beams, but this number is predicted to increase. However, for the bulk of applications, visual inspection of the wood, rather than pre-graded beams, is satisfactory.

Reclaimed flooring includes floorboards, woodblock, wood strip floors, and beams resawn for flooring. The most common product is pine floorboards, with some oak floorboards, temperate and tropical hardwood wood strip and woodblock, and parquet or marquetry. Some pine and oak boards are sold into the furniture and door-making trade for recycling into a new product, such as antique pine dressers or old-style oak ledge and brace doors.

Good quality **architectural woodwork**, such as door surrounds, staircases, cornice, architrave and skirting, is not readily available in reclaimed form. But in 1997, reclaimed materials experts, Salvo, started a complete staircase database, accessible on the internet, to encourage more reuse (www.salvo.co.uk).

Ornamental woodwork, such as carved woodwork, fire surrounds, church interiors, pub and shop interiors, panelling and panelled rooms, is more antique than recycled. Although it is assumed that old woodwork is not destroyed when buildings are demolished or refurbished, this is far from the case – Salvo estimates that at least 20,000 tonnes are destroyed each year. A spectacular example was an entire 17th century panelled room that was dumped in a skip in Soho, London in 1996, which probably had a retail value of around £25,000.

Other commonly available reclaimed items include doors, sawn timber and sundry others. Think imaginatively, and you may well be able to incorporate some reclaimed timber in your home or garden project.

Tips for buying reclaimed timber

- **Always check what is available before designing a project.**
- **Ensure your reclaimed timber is structurally sound.**
- **Opt for wood from older buildings.**
- **Don't buy goods unless you have thoroughly inspected them.**
- **Ensure restoration and/or cleaning work is undertaken by the salvage yard.**
- **Keep the wood's natural surface and avoid new contamination.**
- **Use poorer quality or water-damaged flooring for sheds and lofts.**
- **Be tenacious to get results.**

Tips for buying reclaimed timber

Generally salvage businesses come in two types: those with a shop or showroom mostly selling antique items, and those with an outdoor yard selling reclaimed materials. Many businesses combine both reclaimed and antique. Before visiting check that the business has what you are after.

Identification of reclaimed timber to the species of tree is not always easy. Although some timber at reclaimed yards may be labelled as a particular type, a lot will not.

- **Always check what is available before designing a project**
  For example, check what size doors are easily available from salvage yards before designing your door openings.

- **Ensure your reclaimed timber is structurally sound**
  While all UK retail businesses are covered by UK consumer protection laws, these protect only private buyers, not professional customers, such as builders or designers. Under these consumer protection laws an old wooden beam or reclaimed floorboard, for example, must perform as would be expected, irrespective of a business's general terms and conditions which may disclaim responsibility for "fitness for purpose". But disclaimers written on a sales invoice such as, "This wooden beam is sold for ornamental purposes, without any guarantee, without testing for structural use, and with no checks for

woodworm or rot" could possibly protect the business from liability under consumer protection laws depending on the nature of the goods failure. Although salvage yards will normally reimburse money and take goods back, it is important to be vigilant.

- **Opt for wood from older buildings**
  As a rough rule the better timber is from older buildings. A Victorian pine floor will be made with planks of wood from indigenous first growth forests, giving very dense timber incomparable to the new wood sold these days.

- **Don't buy goods unless you have thoroughly inspected them**
  Check every last detail to make sure you know what you are getting. Take your builder with you if you are unsure about something. Sometimes a pre-wrapped pallet of flooring may look fine on the outside but contain mixed sizes or batches which will make laying expensive. Don't be afraid to ask to look inside packaging; a good dealer will prefer you to check beforehand.

- **Ensure restoration and/or cleaning work is undertaken by the salvage yard**
  If you are going to get woodwork stripped of old paint, ask the yard to do it for you. The paint may contain lead or other chemicals, which yards are often better equipped to deal with than you. Problems can arise if, when the paint is removed, it turns out that a door has been patch-repaired in an unacceptable way. Make sure that any restoration or cleaning work does not commit you to purchase the goods if they turn out to be faulty. On the other hand, some faults must be expected of second-hand goods made from natural materials, so allow some give and take.

- **Keep the wood's natural surface and avoid new contamination**
  Try not to clean or sand away the natural surface of the wood. Old unpainted or unvarnished wood normally only needs wire wooling or scrubbing with soapy water and then waxing with a natural beeswax to bring out the most beautiful finish. In particular, try not to unnecessarily contaminate reclaimed wood with a chemical timber treatment or paint. Bear in mind that natural old timber is usually below the moisture content at which woodworm can thrive.

- **Use poorer quality or water-damaged flooring for sheds and lofts**
  For DIY boarding of non-living areas ask salvage yards if they have any water-damaged, rough quality planking or offcuts (which they usually do). The

price will often be less than chipboard, and although it may involve more work laying, the quality will be better and more durable.

- **Be tenacious to get results**
  Not everyone will see the value of using reclaimed timber or believe that it is feasible, and you may have to insist to architects, builders or craftspeople that it is what you want!

Chemically treated and lead-painted wood

Timber treatments may be used on wood to protect it from decay or pest infestation, and a variety of chemicals have been used for this in the past. According to Salvo, before the 1960s only a small proportion of timber was chemically treated, so most reclaimed timber is uncontaminated.

One exception is lead paint, which can be a problem if the surface of the wood has not been repainted and the paint has become flaky, or when lead painted rooms are being stripped and redecorated. Medecin Sans Frontiers recommend repainting any flaky or dusty old paintwork with modern paint to seal the old paintwork beneath.

As a general precaution, it may be better not to use reclaimed wood for food preparation surfaces, or if you do, then invest in a new untreated wooden chopping block. Do not use creosote-treated railway sleepers indoors; creosote has a very distinctive tarry smell, but if in doubt ask your supplier if wood has been creosoted.

Chapter 3 Timber products and alternatives

As well as straightforward sawn timber, there are a number of different timber products currently available. There is no easy answer as to which is the best environmental option but issues such as forest management, efficient use of resources, the timber's conservation status, energy use in manufacture, pollution, and so on, all need to be considered.

Suitability for the job

Select a timber product suitable for the function it needs to perform but be careful not to over-specify; ie don't use a rare timber from the other side of the world when a locally-sourced, commoner species would serve just as well.

It's important to select a timber product suitable for the function it needs to perform. Strength, stiffness, resistance to splitting, hardness, durability and appearance may all be important factors. Choosing a product that lacks suitable properties for the job (eg, a low durability product for a structure that will be subject to heavy wear) may mean it will need to be replaced rapidly, at a high cost to you and the environment. Even if a longer-lasting timber has a worse initial environmental profile, it may be a better choice than a low durability product in the long term. Conversely, be careful not to over-specify; ie don't use a rare timber from the other side of the world when a locally-sourced, commoner species would serve just as well.

The detailed technical properties of each timber product or type is beyond the scope of this guide, but can be obtained from the product manufacturer, a technical publication (eg *Woods of the World* database on www.forestworld.com), or a timber trade professional. If in doubt, seek advice on suitability from an experienced craftsman, builder or trader.

Appearance

Appearance may be important in some applications, and the darker, red-brown look of tropical timbers, such as mahogany, is often favoured for high-quality furniture and joinery. However, most timber can be effectively stained to achieve a desired tone and you don't have to buy endangered wood to get the look you want. Timber colour also changes with time, lighter softwoods becoming a darker tan colour with age and exposure to sunlight. Older, reclaimed timber often has an attractive style and appearance, as well as being better quality than new wood.

Common timber products

Sawn timber

Sawn timber is the largest product category in the UK. Use of softwood (eg pine, spruce) far outweighs use of hardwood.

Veneers

Veneers are very thin sheets of timber (softwood or hardwood) just millimetres thick, made either by slicing a flat section of timber (sliced veneer) or by rotating a log against a blade (rotary veneer). Veneer is mainly used in plywood production and for decorative purposes on furniture and similar worked items.

Wood-based panels

Wood-based panels (the general name for chipboard, fibreboard, plywood and allied products) are progressively replacing solid timber in a range of applications including furniture, flooring and even joinery. They are generally cheaper to buy and less prone to problems such as shrinkage and irregularities from knots than sawn timber.

Plywood

Plywood is produced by bonding together successive layers of veneers with synthetic glue. It is generally strong (especially in relation to weight), does not split easily and can be bent to form curved surfaces. It can be used for internal or external functions, the main sectors being construction and furniture.

Particleboard / chipboard

This is made by mixing small particles of wood with a synthetic resin and compressing the mixture in a heated press. Chipboard is increasingly used in flooring, panelling, cladding and furniture, the board being coated with a veneer or melamine foil where appropriate to improve appearance.

Cement-bonded particleboard is produced from wood-chip bonded with either Portland or magnesite cement. It has good stability, although boards made with magnesite cement are not suitable for outdoor use since the magnesite has low water resistance. Cement-bonded particleboard has low bending strength and is prone to break during cutting and handling.

Chipboard is an efficient user of residues from forestry thinnings, sawmills and, increasingly, post-consumer wood waste. While the use of waste wood is a positive environmental factor, there is some concern about the health effects of formaldehyde used in the resin (*see Binders in wood-based panels on p22*).

Fibreboard

Fibreboard is made from compressed wood fibres mixed with resin. The two most common types are Medium Density Fibreboard (MDF) and Hardboard. MDF is relatively strong and can be worked into shapes like solid wood, without problems of breaking or splintering. It can be coated with veneer or foils to improve appearance. Hardboard is of a higher density; it has limited strength but is useful as a low-cost material to cover large areas.

Fibreboard is generally not made from post-consumer waste wood, but it does often use forestry thinnings. The same concerns about formaldehyde resins apply as for chipboard. However, one manufacturer in North America (CanFibre) makes MDF from 100 per cent post-consumer waste wood without the use of formaldehyde-containing resin, showing that it is technically possible to do so.

Oriental Strandboard (OSB) and waferboard

OSB is similar to chipboard but stonger and thus suitable for more demanding functions. It is increasingly being used in place of plywood in roofing, flooring etc, and in engineered timber products such as I beams. Waferboard is a similar product.

Structural timber composites

These include glued laminated timber (glulam), laminated veneer lumber (microlam) and parallel strand lumber. They are made from sections of wood glued together into large sections suitable for beams and joists. They are generally stronger than the equivalent size piece of solid timber and have a higher stiffness to weight ratio. Being produced in a controlled environment with a low moisture content, they are also less prone to shrinkage and movement than solid timber.

Structural timber composites can utilise small sections of wood and fast-growing or under-utilised species of tree. However, the energy required for their manufacture and the use of fossil-fuel-derived binders or glues are environmental drawbacks. They are also often expensive.

Binders in wood-based panels

Most wood-based panels (except hardboard, softboard and insulation board) are made with the use of a chemical binder, the most common being urea formaldehyde. Boards containing this binder emit formaldehyde during their life, and concern has been expressed over the contribution this makes to indoor air pollution. The amount of formaldehyde used in boards has been progressively reduced by European manufacturers, and in an average home, emissions from panelboard would be less than one fifth of the World Health Organisation's safe guideline.

Another resin, MDI, is used by some board manufacturers, including some strawboard makers. It is formaldehyde-free and does not give off emissions once the board is manufactured.

While some timber alternatives (ie non-wood boards) have beneficial environmental properties, most have much higher environmental costs associated with their sourcing, production, use or disposal. Their use in place of timber is not recommended.

Timber alternatives

In principle, timber is an environmentally sound material – it is completely natural, renewable, requires low energy for production and, if used correctly, can be long-lasting and a good thermal insulator. The problems with timber arise with the excessive level of demand, the way it is sourced, and the wasteful manner in which it is processed and used.

There are several alternative materials to timber. While some may have beneficial environmental properties, most have much higher environmental costs associated with their sourcing, production, use or disposal. Their use in place of timber is not recommended.

Non-wood boards

Board for partitioning, wall panels, ceilings and door interiors can be made from agricultural by-products, or from waste paper. Since these products are made from residue or waste materials, they have a good environmental profile.

Several companies in the USA manufacture board from straw. It has been estimated that if just 25 per cent of the wheat straw generated annually in the USA were used for this purpose, it would produce enough board to satisfy the entire US demand for particleboard. Some board is manufactured using a binder called MDI (methyl-diphenyl-isocyanate – see above), but some is made without the use of any synthetic resins.

Boards can also be produced from flax coconut fibres or sugar cane residues (the latter is known as bagasse). Flaxboard is light, cheap and a good fire-retardant. It is commonly used for door interiors, although supplies are severely limited and its distinctive odour may be a disadvantage for some functions. Bagasse board manufacturing plants are currently operating in Indonesia, the Philippines, Pakistan and India. One US manufacturer also makes fibreboard from post-consumer recycled newsprint.

Unfortunately, there are currently few supplies of non-wood board in the UK. Small quantities of some products are imported from the continent – *for further details of products available in the UK check the listings section in Chapter 7.*

Steel

Steel is an alternative to timber for construction, in housing frames and load-bearing structures. However, the environmental cost of its manufacture and use is extremely high. The raw materials used (iron ore, limestone, coal and zinc) are all non-renewable and are mined or quarried, with the accompanying destruction of habitat that this involves. Steel manufacture is very energy-intensive and is a major source of dioxin pollutants, thought to be produced largely from recycling steel with PVC coatings. Once in use, steel is also a very poor insulator, resulting in high heat loss from buildings.

PVC

PVC-u (the rigid form of PVC) is a common alternative to timber for window frames and conservatories and has been heavily marketed as long-lasting and low maintenance. However, its production and disposal involve the release of highly poisonous chemicals that are a threat to human health and the environment. Dioxins, persistent chemicals that are known carcinogens and hormone disrupters and accumulate in the food chain, are an unavoidable by-product of PVC production. Lead, cadmium and organotins are used as stabilisers in PVC. When PVC products are disposed of some of these chemicals are again released into the environment. Recycling PVC is fraught with difficulties, and, since recycled PVC-u is of a lower quality but more expensive than virgin material, PVC recycling is currently minimal, and likely to remain so.

Contrary to some beliefs, PVC-u windows do need on-going maintenance, and their life expectancy has been put at 20-25 years, compared with 25-35 years for vacuum-treated softwood.

Aluminium

Aluminium, commonly used for windows and door frames, is produced from a naturally-occurring substance called bauxite in one of the most energy-intensive processes in the world. Although the energy used is often supplied by hydroelectric sources, the large dams and reservoirs required for its generation may displace local communities and disrupt ecosystems.

Bauxite is extracted by opencast mining, requiring the removal of surface vegetation and soil. Producing aluminium from bauxite generates solid residues (including some containing leachable cyanides and fluorides), the disposal of which can contaminate surrounding water courses. Several gases, including flourides, sulphur dioxide and some greenhouse gases, are also produced.

Although the industry makes much of the high recycling levels of aluminium, in 1997 just 30 per cent of the 1.9 million tonnes of aluminium used in Europe came from recycling.

Chapter 4 Buying timber from well-managed forests

If you do need to buy new timber products, choose those that have been certified by the Forest Stewardship Council (FSC) (identified by the distinctive tick tree label). This guarantees your timber comes from a well-managed forest according to internationally-agreed standards. By selecting these products over others, you are sending a powerful message to the timber industry and to governments that you don't want to buy timber that comes from destructive logging. If a shop or timber yard doesn't stock FSC products, ask to see the manager, tell them why you are not buying, and suggest that they should stock FSC products in future.

While there are many certification initiatives on the market or under development (as outlined in this chapter), the FSC is the only scheme that Fauna & Flora International, Friends of the Earth and most other major environmental organisations support.

A credible forest certification and labelling scheme should have all of the following elements:

- **fully participatory, transparent and open processes, including a balanced representation of environmental, social and economic interests**
- **use of performance-based standards**
- **independent, third-party assessment of forest management, with adequate inspections and stakeholder consultation, and on-going monitoring of certified forests**
- **individual forest management units assessed for certification (rather than certification of a whole country or region, for example)**
- **credible chain of custody and labelling system.**

What is forest certification?

Credible, independent information on the source of timber and the impacts of its extraction has generally been unavailable to consumers, making it hard to choose environmentally-sound wood. Certification fills that gap. It involves independent assessment of forest management against a set of agreed standards. Forests meeting the standards are awarded a certificate and products originating from them can be labelled, allowing their preferential selection by consumers.

Two very different types of standards are used in certification schemes. Performance-based standards assess whether pre-determined targets on various aspects of forest management have been met. System or process-based standards assess whether a system is in place to allow forest managers to review and work towards targets they have set themselves. In other words, the process is assessed, but the actual targets or levels of achievement are not.

Although system-based standards may have some uses, particularly for large, complex companies, only a certification system that uses performance-based standards can guarantee a minimum level of good management in a certified forest.

How credible are existing certification schemes?

Table 1 How credible are existing certification schemes?

	Fully participatory and transparent?	Performance-based standards?	Credible inspections and monitoring?	Individual forest units assessed?	Credible label and chain of custody?
Forest Stewardship Council	Yes	Yes	Yes	Yes	Yes
Pan European Forest Certification*	No	Variable	Variable	Variable	Variable
Canadian Standards Association	Variable	No	Yes	Yes	No
Sustainable Forest Initiative	No	No	No	Yes	No

* The Pan European Forest Certification scheme is a collection of national certification systems that differ in their requirements according to country.

The FSC is the only scheme that fulfils all requirements for a credible forest certification scheme, and is the only one recommended by Fauna & Flora International and Friends of the Earth.

Forest Stewardship Council – Global

Fully participatory, transparent and open processes? Yes
Requires a balance of environmental, social and economic interests in all decision-making structures, and transparency is a key element of the system. A summary report on each forest assessment must be publicly available.

Performance-based standards? Yes
Requires the achievement of certain levels before a certificate can be issued.

Rigorous, independent assessment process, including stakeholder consultation and on-going monitoring? Yes
Assessments performed by independent certifying bodies accredited by FSC International, involve document and forest site inspections, and require stakeholder consultation. Annual monitoring after certification.

Individual forest units assessed for certification? Yes
All certification takes place at the forest management unit level.

Credible chain of custody and labelling system? Yes
There is a certified chain of custody of timber from the forest through the processing stages to the retailer, so products carrying the FSC logo are guaranteed to come from a certified forest. Composite products may show percentage of certified wood they contain.

By October 2001 approximately 24 million ha of forest in 48 countries had been certified by the FSC, national standards had been approved in 10 countries – Belgium, Bolivia, Brazil (Terra Firme forests), Canada (Maritime region), Colombia, Germany, Peru, Sweden, UK, USA (Rocky Mountains region), and national working groups or contact persons had been established in a further 18 countries.

Pan European Forest Certification (PEFC) – Europe

Fully participatory, transparent and open processes? No
Schemes have been developed with no or limited input from environmental and social interests. In France, Sweden and Germany, the decision-making structure is such that economic interests can always over-ride the combined vote of social and environmental groups. While summary assessment reports are meant to be available to the public according to the international framework, this is not the case in all countries.

Performance-based standards? Variable
There is no requirement for performance-based standards in the PEFC system and standards vary from country to country. For example, Sweden and Finland use performance-based standards, while in Germany and France system elements are emphasised.

Rigorous, independent assessment process, including stakeholder consultation and on-going monitoring? Variable
Assessments are carried out by third party, nationally accredited bodies, but no required procedures for assessments are specified. In some countries (eg Germany), inspection of the actual forest is not required before a certificate is issued. There is no requirement for stakeholder consultation and variable requirements for monitoring of certified forests.

The PEFC has certified logging in the last remaining old-growth forests in Scandinavia, which environmental groups claim should be protected. It has also certified logging operations that do not respect the grazing rights of the indigenous Saami people, who keep their reindeer in the forests in Scandinavia in winter. In Germany, six whole states have been certified under the PEFC without a certifier visiting the forests.

Individual forest units assessed for certification? Variable
Based on regional certification (with the exception so far of Swedish scheme).

Credible chain of custody and labelling system? Variable
Rules for labelling vary by country.

The CSA has certified clear-cutting in high conservation value forests and logging on indigenous people's lands without their consent.

Canadian Standards Association (CSA) – Canada

Fully participatory, transparent and open processes? Variable
The standard-setting process was open and inclusive. Public input during each forest certification is required via public advisory groups but the views of the group can be (and have been) ignored. Standards are not publicly available free of charge, and there is no requirement for assessment reports to be available.

Performance-based standards? No
The scheme uses a process-based standard with no absolute level of achievement required. Standards to be reached in each forest unit are determined by the forest manager or owner, with advice from a specially convened public advisory group.

Rigorous, independent assessment process, including stakeholder consultation and on-going monitoring? Yes
Requires inspection of documents and the actual forest site, stakeholder consultation and annual monitoring.

Individual forest units assessed for certification? Yes
All certification takes place at the forest management unit level.

Credible chain of custody and labelling system? No
There is currently no label associated with the CSA scheme, but agreement may be reached in the future allowing CSA products to carry the PEFC logo.

The SFI has certified large scale clear-cutting in old-growth temperate rainforest and logging on indigenous people's lands without their consent.

Sustainable Forestry Initiative (SFI) – USA and Canada

Fully participatory, transparent and open processes? No
Standards are set by industry without balanced input from environmental and social interests. Summary assessment reports of each certification should be publicly available, although their content is unspecified and reports have not been available so far.

Performance-based standards? No
The focus of the standards is process-based, although they do include some minimum performance standards. There are no social elements in the standard.

Rigorous, independent assessment process, including stakeholder consultation and on-going monitoring? No
The forest manager can influence the scope and extent of the inspection. No stakeholder consultation is required. Infrequent monitoring (initially after three years, then at five yearly intervals).

Individual forest units assessed for certification? Yes
All certification takes place at the forest management unit level.

Credible chain of custody and labelling system? No
A product label is being developed, but (at the time of writing) without an accompanying chain of custody system, the labelled product will not necessarily originate from certified forest.

Other national certification schemes

Lembaga Ekolabel Indonesia (LEI) – Indonesia
The Indonesian national forest certification system (LEI) is just starting to certify forests, with plans to launch a product label in the near future. The LEI standards are performance-led, include environmental, social and economic considerations and were developed with the involvement of non-government organisations (NGOs). LEI also hopes to gain full mutual recognition by the FSC, so that products from forests certified by LEI could carry the FSC logo.

Malaysian Timber Certification Council (MTCC) – Malaysia
Environmental and social organisations have been participating in the development of a national certification scheme in Malaysia. The goal was to make the scheme compatible with the FSC, but in 2001 most of the major environmental groups withdrew from the process, stating that their views were being ignored and that they no longer supported the system.

There are several other national or regional forest certification schemes, most of which are not yet operational. These are mentioned in the relevant country section in Chapter 5, where applicable.

Note: some forest companies have obtained certification from the International Organisation for Standardisation (ISO) for their system to monitor and improve environmental issues relevant to their business. Such certification is not an assessment of forest management and does not provide any guarantee about the source of timber products the company produces.

Chapter 5 Timber trade – by country

It is not possible to recommend timber from a particular country over that from elsewhere (other than to say timber from closer to home has required less transport from the forest). Management practices and the impact of logging vary from one forest holding to another within the same country, depending on the owner or manager involved. Although a country may have good forest laws, enforcement is often lacking and regulatory institutions desperately under-resourced.

If you are buying new timber products, the best environmental choice is to buy FSC-certified wood. This is the only reliable way to ensure that the timber you choose comes from a well-managed forest and has not contributed to further destruction of the world's forests.

The following information presents a brief snapshot (as of October 2001) of the state of forests in the main countries that supply the UK with timber products, and the progress of certification in these countries. Certification is, however, developing fast and situations may change in the near future.

Table 2 **Major sources of timber products imported into the UK in 1998, by volume**

	Sawn softwood	**Sawn hardwood**	**Plywood**	**Particleboard and fibreboard**
1	Sweden	USA	Indonesia	Belgium-Luxembourg**
2	Latvia	Malaysia	USA	Germany
3	Finland	Latvia	Malaysia	Ireland
4	Russian Federation	Germany	Brazil	Finland
5	Estonia	Italy*	Russian Federation	Spain
6	Canada	Canada	Finland	Portugal
7	Ireland	Cameroon	Canada	France
8	Norway	Sweden	Latvia	USA
9	Lithuania	Ghana	Estonia	Austria
10	Portugal	Cote d'Ivoire	Rep of Korea	Lithuania

* Re-export of timber imported from elsewhere

** Products manufactured largely with wood imported from neighbouring countries

Source: FAO Statistical Database, www.fao.org

Europe

Deforestation is not the issue for most of Europe and forest cover is actually increasing in some parts of the continent. The issue for Europe is forest quality, with intensively-managed planted forest, often using non-native species, making up a high proportion of forest cover, and old, natural forests being increasingly rare. In recent years, policies in most countries have shifted to place more emphasis on restoring natural forests or increasing the natural values of managed areas.

Eastern Europe and European Russia have far more natural forest remaining than the western part of the region. There are fears that the opening up of markets and the accompanying acceleration of logging will destroy or degrade these old, natural forests before their values are fully known and adequate safeguards to protect them are put in place.

UK

Forest cover: approx 10 per cent, 7 per cent conifer plantations (mostly non-native).

Main timber products: sawn softwood (plantation spruce and pine); sawn hardwood (oak, sweet chestnut, beech, ash, sycamore); particleboard and fibreboard.

Main issues: small forest area, particularly of native woodland; high proportion of non-native, single-species plantations; inappropriate positioning of plantations ie places with high value as open ground (policy changes mean this is no longer occurring widely); neglect of native woodland.

Certification: FSC UK national standards approved. The UK Woodland Assurance Scheme (UKWAS) has also developed standards that are fully compliant with FSC requirements – products from UKWAS certified forests may carry the FSC logo. As of October 2001, approximately 65 per cent of the UK's commercial forests were certified under UKWAS / FSC, including the state-managed forests. There is also a group developing certification under the PEFC.

Ireland

Forest cover: approx 9 per cent, mostly non-native conifer plantations.

Main products exported to the UK: fibreboard; softwood logs and sawn timber (pine, spruce).

Main issues: low forest cover; high proportion of non-native single species plantations (efforts now underway to increase broadleaved planting).

Certification: an FSC working group in Ireland has drafted FSC standards for certification, and the state forest service, Coillte, is undergoing FSC certification of its forest holdings. A national certification scheme under PEFC is being developed.

France

Forest cover: approx 28 per cent, mostly semi-natural with a small area of plantation; two-thirds of the forest is broadleaved (dominated by oak and beech), the remainder conifer.

Main products exported to the UK: sawn hardwood (beech, oak).

Main issues: over-emphasis on timber production; low diversity of tree species with equal age trees; over-intensive management.

Certification: small areas of forest have been FSC-certified, although there is no national FSC working group. A national certification scheme under the PEFC is in the final stages of development.

Germany

Forest cover: approx 30 per cent, all officially classified as semi-natural but much of it is planted; two-thirds is coniferous (mainly pine and spruce) and one-third deciduous (dominated by beech and oak).

Main products exported to the UK: particleboard; sawn hardwood (beech, oak).

Main issues: intensive management; high proportion of planted forests with low diversity of tree species (policies to convert plantation-type forests to mixed semi-natural forests now in place).

Certification: national standards for FSC certification have been approved, and several forests are now certified. A PEFC national certification scheme is also running and (as of March 2001) nearly 40 per cent of forests are PEFC certified.

Portugal

Forest cover: approx 40 per cent; three-quarters are semi-natural (principally oak) and one-quarter is plantations, mostly maritime pine and eucalyptus.

Main products exported to the UK: sawn softwood (pine); mostly low-grade timber, used for fencing and pallets.

Main issues: loss of natural forests; establishment of plantations in inappropriate sites (no longer such a problem due to policy changes); exacerbation of fire threat and lowering of water table by plantations.

Certification: there are no FSC-certified forests in Portugal and no national FSC working group. A national certification scheme is being developed under the PEFC.

Scandinavia

Sweden, Finland and Norway are all heavily forested, largely with coniferous forest dominated by Scots pine and Norway spruce. The region's forests have been intensively managed for timber production over many decades, and less than five per cent of old, natural forest (known as old-growth forest) remains. Environmental groups in all three countries have called for the complete protection of these remaining old-growth areas, but they continue to be logged on a sporadic basis.

Sweden

Forest cover: approx 57 per cent, mostly intensively-managed conifer forest.

Main products exported to the UK: sawn softwood (pine, spruce).

Main issues: intensive management reducing natural values; continued logging of few remaining old-growth areas; lack of respect for indigenous Saami people's rights.

Certification: Sweden was the first country to have national FSC standards approved, and a large proportion of the country's forests are now certified under the FSC. There is also a national certification scheme under the PEFC.

Finland

Forest cover: approx 66 per cent, mostly intensively-managed conifer forest.

Main products exported to the UK: sawn softwood (pine, spruce); plywood; particleboard and fibreboard.

Main issues: as in Sweden.

Certification: there is an FSC working group developing national standards, and (as of November 2001) a very small area of forest has been certified by the FSC. A PEFC national certification system has been developed, and (as of March 2001) approximately 65 per cent of Finnish forests are certified under this scheme.

Old-growth logging in Finland certified by PEFC

Most of Finland's forest has been heavily managed for timber production, and just under five per cent of old, natural forest (known as old-growth) remains – some of which continues to be logged. Over 700 plants and animals are nationally threatened as a result.

In 2000 the government forest service logged two sites in an old-growth forest at Pyhävaara in Lapland, ignoring the traditional rights of the indigenous Saami people who used the area as a winter reindeer grazing ground. This was despite being certified under the national PEFC scheme, which claims that "*...certification indicates ... that Finland's forests and forest ecosystems are being sustainably managed*".

A study by environmental groups in January 2001 found over 50 such examples where logging or planned logging that was PEFC certified involved the destruction of old-growth areas or ignored the forest's biological, social or cultural value.

Source: Greenpeace Nordic and Luonto-Liittto (2001) *Anything goes? Report on PEFC Certified Finnish Forestry*. Greenpeace Nordic and Luonto Liitto, Helsinki Finland.

Norway

Forest cover: approx 28 per cent, mostly intensively-managed conifer forest.

Main products exported to the UK: sawn softwood (pine, spruce).

Main issues: as in Sweden, although logging on Saami land is less of an issue in Norway. Special concern over valuable unprotected mountain and coastal forests.

Certification: there is no FSC working group in Norway, but a small area of forest has been certified under the FSC. Approximately three-quarters of productive forest in Norway have been certified under the PEFC scheme (originally developed as part of a Living Forest's Project).

Baltic States

The Baltic States are all moderately forested, but due to a long period of exploitation, there are few undisturbed old-growth forests. There is a large percentage of natural (rather than planted) forest that is of high value for biodiversity, and a varying amount of forest over 100 years old.

Since independence from Russia, much of the forest is being returned to private ownership. The forestry sector has changed enormously, and the region is now a major supplier of timber to western Europe. Illegal logging and corruption is a problem, which is exacerbated by under-resourced regulatory institutions and poor forest inventories. There is a danger that the valuable areas for biodiversity are being logged before they are recognised.

Latvia

Forest cover: approx 44 per cent, almost all semi-natural (60 per cent coniferous) with a small area of plantation.

Main products exported to the UK: sawn softwood (pine, spruce).

Main issues: small size of private forest holdings following land reform (over 90 per cent of private forest properties predicted to be no bigger than five hectares); lack of knowledge of forest management by new forest owners; rapid growth in timber industry coupled with lack of information on biodiversity values of forest; illegal practices; lack of capacity in regulatory bodies.

Certification: a small area of forest has been certified under the FSC and there is a working group developing national standards. A national certification scheme under the PEFC is close to being operational.

Estonia

Forest cover: approx 42 per cent; mostly semi-natural (two-thirds coniferous) with a small area of plantation.

Main products exported to the UK: sawn softwood (pine, spruce).

Main issues: as in Latvia.

Certification: a small number of forests have been certified under the FSC and a working group is developing national standards. There are also moves to start development of a certification scheme under the PEFC.

Lithuania

Forest cover: approx 30 per cent, mostly semi-natural (60 per cent coniferous), with a small area of plantation.

Main products exported to the UK: sawn softwood (pine, spruce).

Main issues: as in Latvia.

Certification: there are no forests certified by the FSC and no FSC Working Group, but the State Forest Service has started moves towards FSC certifying its forests.

Russia

Forest cover: approx 50 per cent, largely natural forest, both coniferous and broadleaved. Contains nearly one-fifth of the world's total forest area and one-quarter of remaining frontier forests (mostly in Siberia). The European region of Russia hosts the only remaining large tracts of old-growth forest in Europe.

Main exports to the UK: sawn softwood (pine, spruce); plywood.

Main issues: rapid expansion of logging companies into untouched forests in Russian Far East (Siberia); widespread illegal practices and corruption (20 per cent of timber logged is estimated to violate legislation); weak legislation and lack of capacity in regulatory institutions; recent abolition of Forest Department and transfer of responsibilities to Ministry of Natural Resources; lack of local processing and benefit from logging to communities; logging of old-growth forests (several companies have agreed to a moratorium on logging in old-growth areas in western Russia).

Certification: a small area of forest has been FSC certified, and a working group is developing national standards. Discussions on a government-led national certification scheme have been held, and there are attempts to incorporate this under PEFC.

North America

North America has vast forest areas and is the world's leading timber-producing region. Much timber is extracted from natural forest, some previously unlogged. Forest allocation for commercial exploitation, the huge quantities cut and the logging methods have been highly controversial. Global demand for wood products is driving the industry into remote areas; large areas of far northern Canada's coniferous forest are now slated for cutting.

Canada

Forest cover: approx 27 per cent, almost all natural forest, including vast coniferous forests in the north (boreal forest), and important temperate rainforest in the west. Canada has the third largest area of forest in the world (after Russia and Brazil) and contains a quarter of the world's remaining frontier forests.

Main products exported to the UK: sawn softwood (spruce, pine, fir, hemlock, cedar); sawn hardwood (white and red oak, hard maple, ash, cherry, tulipwood); industrial roundwood; plywood.

Main issues: large scale clear-cutting of temperate rainforests; violation of forest regulations; logging on indigenous land; rapid expansion of logging. But protection of large area of temperate rainforest on mainland coast of British Colombia (the Great Bear Rainforest) announced in April 2001.

Certification: there are some FSC-certified forests in Canada, and FSC standards have been approved for the east coast (Maritime) region. Canada has developed its own certification scheme under the Canadian Standards Association and large areas of forest have been certified.

Logging and injustice in British Colombia

The Elaho valley in British Colombia is clothed in old growth temperate rainforest. It is the only remaining valley in the area with significant numbers of ancient Douglas fir and western red cedar trees, with individuals up to 1,000 years old. The valley is rich in other biodiversity too, including large mammals such as the grizzly bear, black bear, wolf and cougar.

Since 1997, giant timber company Interfor has been logging the Elaho valley, including the ancient trees. This has generated enormous controversy among environmentalists and the people of the Squamish First Nation, in whose territory the valley falls. In autumn 1999, protesters trying to stop the logging were attacked and beaten in their campsite by loggers. Although five men were found guilty of the attack, they received only suspended sentences. In contrast two protesters that participated in a peaceful blockade were sentenced to one year in jail; their sentences were later reduced on appeal.

Source: Western Canada Wilderness Committee Website: www.wildernesscommittee.org

USA

Forest cover: approx 25 per cent, largely semi-natural, with coniferous species (eg pine, spruce, Douglas fir) dominating in the west and south, and broadleaved species (eg oak, maple, hickory, beech) more common in the east. Less than one-tenth of the forest remains undisturbed, chiefly in Alaska and the west.

Main products exported to the UK: sawn hardwood (white and red oak, hard maple, ash, cherry, tulipwood); plywood; industrial roundwood.

Main issues: extent of logging in state-owned national forests; bias of government forest service to timber interests; subsidisation of timber industry through funding for logging roads; old-growth logging. Positive legislation passed to end logging and roadbuilding in one-third of national forest in 2001, but may be watered down by new administration.

Certification: almost one per cent of forest in the USA has been certified under the FSC, and a national working group is developing standards for certification. Forest certification has also been developed under the Sustainable Forest Initiative of the American Forest and Paper Association and over 11 million ha of forests in the USA and Canada have been certified under this scheme.

South-east Asia
Many south-east Asian countries have lost a significant proportion of their forest cover during the past half century, due to rapid logging and other pressures. Driven by international demand, countries such as Thailand and the Philippines, once major players in the international timber market, have destroyed or degraded so much forest that their timber industries have shrunk dramatically. The region remains a very large producer of wood products, however, with Malaysia and Indonesia among the leading countries in the international timber trade.

Malaysia

Forest cover: approx 59 per cent, mostly natural forest with a small area of plantation.

Major timber products exported to the UK: plywood; sawn hardwood (meranti, keruing, kapur).

Main issues: unsustainable harvesting levels in Sarawak and Sabah (sustainable management is better developed in Peninsula Malaysia); logging on indigenous land and suppression of opposition; depletion of major timber species; processing and export of illegal timber from Indonesia (an estimated 35 per cent of timber exports are illegal at source).

Certification: the Malaysian Timber Certification Council has been developing a forest certification scheme, and is seeking mutual recognition from the FSC. There is no national FSC group. One natural forest in Sabah has received FSC certification.

Sustainable timber harvesting in the Pacific

The forests of the Solomon Islands and nearby Papua New Guinea are the third largest pristine tropical rainforest on Earth and the largest remaining area of intact rainforest in the Asia-Pacific region. During the 1980s, largely Asian-based timber companies started logging these forests at three times the estimated sustainable rate, with dire environmental and social impacts. Large areas of forest were destroyed or severely degraded, coral reefs were smothered by soil run-off from the exposed ground, and the livelihoods of local forest-dependent communities were ruined.

Seeing these devastating impacts, several local communities resisted the pressure from industrial logging and, with help from local and international NGOs, set-up schemes to manage their forests and harvest the timber themselves on a sustainable basis. Some of the schemes have received FSC certification, and the timber is in high demand on the international market, as well as being used to improve local housing. The profit the communities receive per tree is 10 times the royalty payment offered by logging companies, and the forest is managed so that it can continue to provide a source of income for future generations.

Sources: Greenpeace websites: www.greenpeace.org; www.greenpeace.org.au
Rainforest Medical Bulletin, www.xs4all.nl/~rainmed

Indonesia

Forest cover: 49 per cent closed forest, mostly natural forest with some plantation.

Main products exported to the UK: plywood; sawn hardwood (meranti, seraya, ramin (until banned in 2001)).

Main issues: rapid deforestation; complete loss of government control of forests outside Java; massive illegality (over 70 per cent of timber is estimated to be illegally sourced); corruption and cronyism; conversion of natural forest to plantations; over-capacity in the timber processing industry; violation of indigenous peoples' rights and suppression of opposition.

Certification: Indonesia is developing its own forest certification scheme, Lembaga Ekolabel Indonesia (LEI), which is seeking mutual recognition with the FSC. A few areas of forest have been certified by the FSC. However, several Indonesian NGOs have expressed concern about certification proceeding at all in the climate of illegality, corruption and disrespect for the rights of local communities that currently characterises the forest industry in Indonesia.

Illegal logging and corruption in Indonesian national park

Tanjung Puting national park covers an area of 400,000 ha in central Kalimantan, Indonesia. It contains a range of forest habitats and is home to over 200 bird species, 29 mammal, and nine primate species, including 2,000 of the seriously-threatened orangutan.

Illegal logging, mainly for ramin timber, has been occurring in the southern and eastern parts of the park for some time, but has spread into the very core of the park, in full view of the authorities, tourist lodges and research stations. As stocks of ramin have become depleted, other timbers such as meranti have also started to be cut. Corruption among park rangers, police and military allows the illegal logging to flourish. The head of the park believes that if the current rate of logging continues, the park, together with the rare orangutans and other invaluable biodiversity, will disappear within five years. The situation in Tanjung Puting is mirrored in many of Indonesia's supposedly protected areas.

Source: Environmental Investigations Agency (1999) *The Final Cut*. EIA, London.

Africa

West Africa has had a very active timber industry for many decades and forests in several countries have been extensively destroyed or degraded, with stocks of many of the most popular timber species (eg, khaya, sapele, afrormosia, wawa, iroko) seriously depleted. Efforts are now underway to manage some remaining areas of forest sustainably. Liberia holds the largest areas of unexploited forest in west Africa, but this too is now being logged at an alarming rate.

The forests of the Congo Basin in central Africa (including Cameroon, Gabon, and the Democratic Republic of Congo) are the second largest tropical forest area in the world (after the Amazon Basin), and have so far been less exploited than those in west Africa. They are vital refuges for many species of plant and animal as well as home to many millions of people. However, the timber industry is beginning to open up the forest to logging and settlers, causing great concern for the region's future.

Cote d'Ivoire (Ivory Coast)

Forest cover: approx 22 per cent, largely natural forest with some plantations (teak and other).

Main products exported to the UK: sawn hardwood (iroko, utile, sapele, khaya).

Main issues: high proportion of forests destroyed and degraded; intensive logging and depletion of major timber species over several decades; current harvesting of small dimension trees (in violation of legislation); short duration of concession allocations (five years) gives no incentive for long-term management.

Certification: there are no FSC-certified forests and no national FSC working group. The country is a member of the African Timber Organisation, which has been working on a certification scheme.

Ghana

Forest cover: approx 28 per cent, largely natural forest with a modest area of plantation (mainly teak).

Main products exported to the UK: sawn hardwood (wawa, iroko, utile, sapele, khaya).

Main issues: high proportion of forests destroyed and degraded; intensive logging and depletion of favoured species over several decades, but sustainable management is now being attempted; illegal logging an issue during the 1990s.

Certification: there are no FSC certified forests in Ghana, but there is an FSC national contact person. Ghana is in the process of developing a national forest certification scheme. A computerised log tracking project is also under development. Ghana is a member of the African Timber Organisation, which has been developing a certification scheme.

Cameroon

Forest cover: approx 51 per cent, largely natural forest with a modest area of plantations.

Main products exported to the UK: sawn hardwood (sapele, iroko, utile).

Main issues: logging currently opening up last remaining tracts of primary forest; high level of illegality (50 per cent of logging estimated to be illegal); lack of capacity of regulatory institutions; dependence of industry on small number of timber species; minimal local processing to add value in-country.

Certification: there are no FSC certified forests, but there is a national FSC working group developing standards. Cameroon is a member of the African Timber Organisation, which has been developing a certification scheme.

European companies and illegal logging in Cameroon

Illegal logging and corruption are rife in Cameroon's forestry sector. Senior political and military figures are heavily involved in the timber industry, hindering efforts to enforce the forest laws. In 1999 a government inspection found that all but one of the logging companies in the East Province (including one Italian and four French companies) were operating illegally.

An NGO investigation of the Cameroon Forestry Company, a subsidiary of the French company Thanry, found a host of illegal practices. These included concession boundaries being disregarded by the loggers, logging in unauthorised areas and logging of trees below the minimum-allowed diameter. Social provisions did not meet legal requirements, with a lack of basic facilities for workers and inadequate health and safety practices. The company's turnover from illegal logging was estimated at more than US$4 million.

The environmental and social impacts of the logging were also severe, including increased soil erosion and blocked or silted rivers. It is predicted that the most heavily logged tree species, including three that are globally threatened (sapele, utile/sipo, afrormosia) are likely to disappear from the area in the medium term. Non-timber forest products available to the local villagers are decreasing: the sapele tree, for example, harbours a caterpillar that is collected by the local people and sold, but it is becoming scarcer as logging removes the sapele trees.

Sources: Forests Monitor (2001) *Sold down the river. The need to control transnational forestry corporations: a European case study.* Forests Monitor, Cambridge, UK.

Verbelen, F. (2000) *Cameroon government expresses concern over illegal logging by European companies.* FERN, Moreton-in-Marsh, UK, www.fern.org

---

Gabon

Forest cover: approx 85 per cent, almost all natural forest.

Main products exported to the UK: sawn hardwood (okoumé).

Main issues: rapid increase in logging, high level of illegality; reliance of timber industry on single species (okoumé); fears over regeneration of okoumé; low financial revenue to country from logging; lack of capacity of government forest department; lack of in-country processing.

Certification: there are no FSC-certified forests nor an FSC working group. Gabon is part of the African Timber Organisation, which is developing a certification scheme.

Brazil

Forest cover: approx 64 per cent, mainly natural forest. Contains the largest area of tropical rainforest in the world, the Amazon Basin, important Atlantic coastal forest and araucaria forest. Also approx five million ha of plantations, largely pine and eucalyptus.

Main products exported to the UK: plywood; sawn hardwood (Brazilian mahogany, South American cedar, virola).

Main issues: destruction of araucaria forest (reduced to 18 per cent of original area) and Atlantic forest (reduced to five per cent); increase in deforestation rate in Amazon; securing of large-scale logging concessions by Asian logging companies, resulting in fears over increased logging; high level of illegality (government estimates that 80 per cent of timber from the Amazon is illegally logged); forest fires; invasion of indigenous reserves and damage to forest to extract Brazilian mahogany; (mahogany logging and trade temporarily banned by government in 2001); lack of capacity of regulatory body IBAMA.

Certification: several plantations and a small amount of natural forest have been certified under the FSC and an FSC working group is developing national standards (standards for one type of forest are already approved). There is also a national certification scheme, Cerflor, under development, but it does not have the support of environmental groups.

The illegal mahogany trail – from Brazil to the UK

In 1995, two UK journalists, posing as researchers, witnessed the illegal felling and extraction of Brazilian mahogany trees inside the Xikram do Catetê indigenous people's reserve in the state of Pará (logging within Indian reserves is illegal). The journalists covertly marked some of the sawn timber and accompanied it to the port at Belem, from where it was to be shipped to the UK.

Although alerted to the illegal timber, the government agency in charge of environmental affairs, IBAMA, took no action and gave the consignment an export permit. The importing company in the UK was also alerted to the illegality of the timber they were receiving. The company, NORDISK, is supposedly committed not to deal in timber from Indian reserves through signature of a voluntary agreement known as AIMEX. However, the company took no action and sold the timber on to outlets in the UK.

Since 1996, the Brazilian government has had a moratorium on new licences for mahogany logging (although existing licences could continue to operate). In 2001, recognising the high level of illegality in the trade, the government temporarily banned all mahogany logging and trade in Brazil.

Source: Hering, R. and Tanner, S. (1997). *Plunder for Profit. The UK and Brazilian mahogany trade.* Friends of the Earth, London, UK.

South America

South America contains the largest area of tropical forest in the world, the Amazon Basin, as well as a range of other forest areas and types. The situation varies enormously across the region, but only three countries (Brazil, Guyana and Chile) currently export a significant quantity of timber to the UK. As the pressure on forests continues to grow, there are great concerns that deforestation and degradation in some of the remaining large tracts of intact forest will increase rapidly.

Guyana

Forest cover: approx 79 per cent, all natural forest.

Main products exported to the UK: sawn hardwood (greenheart).

Main issues: acceleration of logging as large international companies attempt to secure concessions; lack of capacity of government forest regulatory institutions; dependence of timber industry on single species (greenheart); lack of in-country processing.

Certification: there are no FSC-certified forests, and no FSC working group.

Chile

Forest cover: approx 21 per cent, both natural forest dominated by southern beeches or broadleaf evergreens, and extensive plantations, largely pine with some eucalyptus.

Main products exported to the UK: sawn softwood (pine).

Main issues: over-exploitation of key species; conversion of natural forest to plantations; logging of native forests for woodchip (largely for export to Japan); expulsion of rural population, increased soil erosion and lowering of water table due to plantations.

Certification: an FSC working group is developing national standards, and a small area of forest has been FSC certified.

Chapter 6 A-Z of timbers

Sometimes a suitable timber for a specific job will simply not be available in reclaimed form or with FSC certification, and you may be left with the difficult decision of selecting uncertified wood. FSC certification of forests has so far had the most up-take in northern countries such as Sweden, and although there are certified tropical timbers available *(contact the suppliers included in Chapter 7, or see www.fsc-uk.demon.co.uk for an up-to-date list)*, they remain in short supply. If you cannot find a timber appropriate for your purposes that is certified, follow the advice below and use the A-Z table below and the country information in Chapter 5 to help you make the best environmental choice.

Find out the timber type

Always check with your architect, builder or supplier whether it's possible to use reclaimed or FSC certified timber in the first instance. If this is not possible, find out the origin and type of the proposed timber at the earliest possible stage. Names such as mahogany may be used to refer to a mahogany-type hardwood, rather than wood from an actual mahogany tree, so insist that you're told the precise timber type. Many species are also traded under several different names so if you can't find a timber in the A-Z, ask for alternative trade names or the scientific name.

Insist on an alternative timber, if necessary

If you're unhappy about the proposed timber because of its conservation status or country of origin, don't be afraid to push for an alternative type. Species that are listed as globally threatened, especially those in the higher conservation categories of Critically Endangered or Endangered, are of special concern and unless they are FSC certified, alternatives should always be sought. Remember, though, that even if a timber isn't listed as threatened, its extraction may still have caused serious negative impacts.

Some timbers are associated with very specific end uses, and certain woods may be used for particular functions out of convention or familiarity within the trade. These timbers may be suffering from decades of over-exploitation, but there may well be other, less-threatened species that have the same properties and could be used in their place. The commercialisation of lesser-used species has been the subject of much debate and, while it is important to ensure that these lesser-known trees don't suffer the same fate as many of the traditionally exploited woods, using a wider range of timbers from a well-managed source can help take the pressure off severely-depleted species.

Detailed technical information on the properties of individual timber species is outside the scope of this guide, but it can be readily obtained from elsewhere (eg *Woods of the World* on www.forestworld.com, or ask a timber trade professional). Remember that, as a general rule, timber from close to home is preferable to that from a great distance, as less fossil fuel will have been used to transport it.

About the A-Z table

The A-Z table covers the most commonly used timbers in the UK, as well as some lesser-used species. Timbers are listed alphabetically according to the type of tree, for example American Cedar is listed under Cedar, American. If a timber is not listed here, you can check if it is globally threatened by consulting the Tree Conservation Information Service on the UNEP-World Conservation Monitoring Centre's website: www.unep-wcmc.org/trees/index.html

There is a much greater variety of hardwoods used in the timber trade than softwoods (reflecting the diversity of the tropical forest where many hardwood species originate), although volumes of hardwood used in the UK are much less. Softwoods are identified as such in the table, all remaining timbers listed are hardwoods. Note that the terms softwood and hardwood relate to the type of tree, hardwood timber coming generally from broadleaved trees (angiosperms) and softwood from coniferous trees (gymnosperms). Although in most instances hardwoods tend to be harder and more durable than softwoods, this is not always the case. Balsa, for example, is classified as a hardwood although it is extremely soft, and pitch pine, technically a softwood, is a very hard, durable timber. The level of use in the UK is indicative only.

Categories of threat

These are taken from the *World List of Threatened Trees* (*see Further Information in Chapter 8*), which has recently been incorporated into the 2000 IUCN Red List (the "official" list of globally threatened species). The threat categories reflect the status of the species throughout its range. Some species may also be threatened in individual countries, but space does not permit inclusion of all national threat classifications here.

CR – Critically Endangered: a very high risk of extinction in the wild.
EN – Endangered: a high risk of extinction in the wild.
VU – Vulnerable: at risk of extinction in the wild.
LR (nt) – Lower Risk (near threatened): close to qualifying as Vulnerable.

CITES
CITES (The Convention on International Trade in Endangered Species of Wild Fauna and Flora) is an international agreement aimed at regulating the trade in wildlife (*see Appendix*). Species can be listed on one of three appendices:

Appendix I – bans all international trade (except in exceptional circumstances eg, for scientific research)
Appendix II – international trade requires an export permit, which can only be issued if the trade will not be detrimental to the survival of the species. Import into Europe also requires a permit
Appendix III – international trade is subject to certain export conditions.

Listing on Appendices I and II applies to the species in all countries where it occurs; listings on Appendix III apply only to the countries specified.

Table 3 A-Z of timbers

Common name	Scientific name	Origin	Uses
Abura	*Mitragyna ciliata*	West Africa	Interior joinery
Afara	*Terminalia superba*	Africa	Plywood, interior use
Afrormosia	*Pericopsis elata*	West Africa	Furniture, joinery
Afzelia	*Afzelia* spp.	West Africa	Top quality exterior joinery
Agba	*Gossweilerodendron balsamiferum*	West Africa	Plywood, furniture
Alder	*Alnus glutinosa*	UK, Europe	Minor utility products
Alstonia	*Alstonia* spp.	Africa	Various, depending on density
Andiroba	*Carapa guianensis*	South America	Turnery
Andoung	*Monopetalanthus spp.*	Africa	Furniture, light construction, plywood, boxes and crates
Antiaris	*Antiaris* spp.	Africa	Veneer, plywood, furniture, joinery, boxes and crates, light construction
Asanfona	*Aningeria* spp.	Africa	Musical instruments, heavy construction, marine, furniture, flooring
Ash	*Fraxinus* spp.	UK, Europe, North America	Light coloured furniture, panelling, tool handles
Apple	*Malus sylvestris*	UK, Europe	Minor craft items
Ayan	*Distemonanthus benthamianus*	Africa	Outdoor construction, marine construction, furniture, decorative veneers
Balau / Selangan batu /Bangkirai	*Shorea* spp.	South-east Asia	Heavy duty construction work
Balsa	*Ochroma lagopus*	Ecuador	Model making, insulation
Basralocus	*Dicornia guianensis*	South America	Marine and dock work
Basswood, American	*Tilia americana*	North America	Turnery, minor items
Beech	*Fagus* spp.	UK, Europe, North America	Furniture, flooring, musical instruments
Berlinia, red	*Berlinia* spp.	Africa	Heavy construction, furniture and cabinetwork, veneers, panelling

Key to threat status CR – Critically Endangered EN – Endangered VU – Vulnerable LR (nt) – Lower Risk

Level of use in the UK	Global threat status	Available as reclaimed?
Minor	–	
Minor	–	
Minor	EN; CITES Appx II	
Minor	*A. africana* VU *A. bipindensis* VU *A. pachyloba* VU	
Minor	EN	
Minor	–	Occasionally, as beams
Minor	–	
Minor	–	
Minor	*M. durandii* VU *M. compactus* VU *M heitzii* LR (nt)	
Minor	–	
Minor	–	
Major	–	Occasionally, as flooring
Minor	–	
Minor	–	
Major	Many *Shorea* spp. in international trade are CR, EN or VU	
Minor	–	
Minor	–	
Minor	–	
Major	–	Regularly, as wood strip and woodblock flooring
Minor	*B. occidentalis* VU	

Common name	Scientific name	Origin	Uses
Bintangor	*Calophyllum* spp.	South-east Asia	General purpose timber, musical instruments
Binuang	*Octomeles sumatrana*	South-east Asia	Plywood, light construction, furniture components, cabinet work
Birch	*Betula* spp.	UK, Europe, North America	General purpose timber, plywood
Black bean	*Castanospermum australe*	Australia	Furniture, cabinet work, joinery
Black locust	*Robinia pseudoacacia*	Europe, America	Poles, agricultural implements, furniture
Blackbutt	*Eucalyptus pilularis*	Australia	General purpose timber, construction (including marine), flooring
Blackwood, African	*Dalbergia melanoxylon*	Africa	Musical instruments, craft products
Blue gum	*Eucalyptus saligna*	Australia	General purpose timber, also used for paper
Boxwood, European	*Buxus sempervirens*	Europe	Turnery, craftwork, sports goods, musical instruments
Bubinga	*Copaifera salikounda*	West Africa	Veneer, furniture
Caimito	*Pouteria* spp.	South America	Light construction, furniture, cabinet work
Canarium	*Canarium schweinfurthii*	Africa	Light construction, furniture, veneer, plywood.
Cedar, American	*Cedrela* spp.	South and Central America	Cabinet making, boatbuilding, light construction
Cedar, pencil (softwood)	*Juniperus virginiana*/ *J. procera*	*J. virginiana*: North America *J. procera*: East Africa	Specialist uses
Cedar, western red (softwood)	*Thuja plicata*	North America, some UK plantations	Exterior use, cladding
Celtis	*Celtis* spp.	Africa	Furniture, cabinets, carving, veneer
Cherry, European	*Prunus* spp.	UK, Europe, North America	Specialised crafted furniture and decorative work, musical instruments
Chestnut, horse	*Aesculus hippocastanum*	UK, Europe	Minor goods, turnery and utensils
Chestnut, sweet	*Castanea sativa*	UK, Europe	Furniture, joinery, fencing
Chontaquiro	*Diplotropis martiussi*	South America	Outdoor and marine construction
Coigue	*Nothofagus dombeyi*	South America	Furniture, joinery, mouldings, turnery
Cordia	*Cordia millenii*	Africa	Exterior cladding, furniture, joinery

Key to threat status CR – Critically Endangered EN – Endangered VU – Vulnerable LR (nt) – Lower Risk

Level of use in the UK	Global threat status	Available as reclaimed?
Minor	Some species are threatened	
Minor	–	
Minor	–	
Minor	–	
Minor	–	
Minor	–	
Minor	LR (nt)	
Minor	–	Occasionally, as wood strip flooring
Minor	–	
Minor	VU	Regularly, as woodblock flooring
Minor	Several species are threatened	
Minor	–	
Minor	*C. odorata* VU, CITES Appdx III (Peruvian population) *C. fissilis* EN *C. lilloi* EN	
Minor	*J. procera* LR (nt)	
Minor	–	Regularly, as beams
Minor	–	
Minor	–	
Minor		Regularly, as beams
Minor		Regularly, as beams
Minor	–	
Minor	–	
Minor	–	

Common name	Scientific name	Origin	Uses
Cottonwood	*Bombax* spp.	Africa	Plywood, blockboard, boxes and crates, furniture
Curupay / Curapixa	*Anadenanthera macrocarpa*	South America	Heavy construction, flooring, turnery
Dafo	*Terminalia brassii*	South-east Asia	Veneer, furniture, cabinet work, joinery,
Dahoma	*Piptadeniastrum africanum*	Africa	Heavy construction, wharf decking, flooring
Danta	*Nesogordonia papaverifera*	Africa	Furniture, turnery, flooring, tool handles
Denya	*Cyclicodiscus gabunensis*	Africa	External construction
Durian	*Durio* spp.	South-east Asia	Furniture, veneer, plywood, light construction
Ebony	*Diospyros* spp.	Africa, Asia	Cutlery handles, musical instruments, craftwork.
Ekki / Azobe / Kaku	*Lophira alata*	West Africa	Sea defences, sleepers
Elm	*Ulmus* spp.	UK, Europe, North America	Furniture, joinery, flooring, external cladding
Fir, Douglas (softwood)	*Pseudotsuga taxifolia / P. menziesii*	UK, Europe (plantations) North America	Plywood, structural work, sea defences
Fir, silver (softwood)	*Abies alba*	UK (plantations), Northern Europe	Building, joinery, packaging
Freijo	*Cordia goeldiana*	South America	Joinery, veneer, construction
Fromager	*Ceiba pentandra*	Africa, South America	Veneer, weak packaging
Gmelina	*Gmelina arborea*	Native to South Asia, timber is from tropical plantations	Light construction, packaging, furniture
Gombe	*Didelotia* spp.	Africa	Plywood, blockboard, veneers, particleboard, furniture, joinery
Greenheart	*Chlorocardium rodiei / Ocotea rodiei*	Guyana	Sea defences
Guarea	*Guarea cedrata / Guarea thompsonii*	Central and West Africa	Furniture and exterior work
Hemlock, western (softwood)	*Tsuga heterophylla*	UK, Europe (plantations) North America	Construction
Hickory	*Carya* spp.	North America	Sports goods, tool handles, drum sticks
Holly	*Ilex aquifolium*	UK, Europe	Craft work, inlays

Key to threat status CR – Critically Endangered EN – Endangered VU – Vulnerable LR (nt) – Lower Risk

Level of use in the UK	Global threat status	Available as reclaimed?
Minor	–	
Minor	–	
Minor	–	
Minor	–	
Minor	VU	
Minor	–	
Minor	Several species are VU	
Minor	Several species in international trade are EN or VU	Regularly, as antique escutcheons, door knobs
Minor	VU	Occasionally, as woodblock flooring
Minor	–	Regularly, as floorboards
Major	–	Regularly, as floorboards
Minor	–	
Minor	–	
Minor	–	
Minor	–	
Minor	*D. idae* LR (nt) *D. unifoliolata* LR (nt)	
Minor	VU	Regularly, as beams
Minor	*G. cedrata* VU *G. thompsonii* VU	
Minor	–	
Minor	–	
Minor	–	

Common name	Scientific name	Origin	Uses
Hornbeam	*Carpinus betulus*	UK, Europe	Minor items, musical instruments
Hyedua	*Guibourtia ehie*	West Africa	Interior construction, furniture, veneer, turnery
Idigbo / Emeri / Framire	*Terminalia ivorensis*	West Africa	Joinery and outdoor work
Ilomba	*Pycnanthus angolensis*	Africa	General utility timber, furniture components, interior joinery, plywood
Imbuja	*Phoebe / Ocotea porosa*	South America	Interior construction, furniture
Ipe Peroba/ Ipe de Campos	*Paratecoma peroba*	South America	Furniture, interior joinery, decking, flooring, vats and tanks, veneers
Iroko / Odum / Mvule	*Milicia excelsa*	Africa	Garden furniture, boat building, flooring and joinery
Izombe	*Testulea gabonensis*	Africa	Turnery
Jacareuba	*Calophyllum* spp.	South America	General purpose timber, musical instruments
Jarrah	*Eucalyptus marginata*	Australia	Outdoor construction, flooring, decking, sleepers
Jelutong	*Dyera costulata*	South-east Asia	Interior work, crafts, pattern making
Jequitiba	*Cariniana* spp.	South America	Construction, furniture
Kapur	*Dryobalanops* spp.	South-east Asia (Indonesia, Malaysia)	Exterior joinery and construction
Karri	*Eucalyptus diversicolor*	Australia	Heavy duty outdoor construction, sleepers
Kauvula	*Endospermum medullosum*	South-east Asia	Furniture parts, minor items
Kempas	*Koompassia malaccensis*	South-east Asia	Heavy construction uses
Keruing / Yang / Curjun	*Dipterocarpus* spp.	Indonesia, Malaysia	Strength applications in hidden work in furniture, building, transport decking, plywood
Khaya – see Mahogany, African			
Kokoti	*Anopyxis klaineana*	Africa	Underwater construction and piling
Kosipo / Omu	*Entandrophragma candollei*	Africa	Furniture, flooring
Koto	*Pterygota spp*	Africa	Veneer, interior joinery, furniture
Kussia – see Opepe			
Larch (softwood)	*Larix decidua*	UK (plantations) Europe, Russia	General purpose timber

Key to threat status CR – Critically Endangered EN – Endangered VU – Vulnerable LR (nt) – Lower Risk

Level of use in the UK	Global threat status	Available as reclaimed?
Minor	–	
Minor	VU	
Minor	VU	
Minor	–	
Minor	VU	
Minor	–	
Major	LR (nt)	Regularly, as wood strip and woodblock flooring
Minor	EN	
Minor	–	Regularly, as wood strip and woodblock flooring, occasionally as beams
Minor	–	
Minor	–	
Minor	*D.aromatica* CR Some other species EN	
Minor	–	Regularly, as wood strip and woodblock flooring, occasionally as beams
Minor	–	
Minor	–	
Major	Many species in international trade are CR, EN	Regularly, as flooring
Minor	VU	
Minor	VU	
Minor	*P. macrocarpa* VU *P. bequaertii* VU	
Major	–	

Common name	Scientific name	Origin	Uses
Latandza	*Albizia ferruginea*	Africa	Heavy construction, furniture, marine work, veneer
Lati	*Amphimas* spp.	Africa	Interior joinery, veneer, mouldings
Laurel, Chilean	*Laurelia aromatica*	South America	Veneer
Lignum vitae	*Guaiacum* spp.	Central and South America	Special bearings, tools, sports goods
Limbali	*Gilbertiodendron* spp.	Africa	Construction (including marine), industrial flooring, panelling
Lime	*Tilia* spp.	Europe	Brush backs, turnery, minor goods
Longui	*Chrysophyllum africana*	Africa	General purpose timber
Louro (see also Greenheart)	*Ocotea* spp.	South America	Marine structures, heavy duty work
Mahogany, African	*Khaya ivorensis*	West Africa	Utility and decorative work, indoors and outdoors, from boat building to furniture and joinery.
Mahogany, Brazilian	*Swietenia macrophylla*	Central and South America	Joinery, high quality furniture, plywood
Makarati	*Burkea africana*	Africa	Flooring, furniture, joinery
Makore	*Tieghemella heckelii*	West Africa	Joinery and wood work subjected to tough environments
Mansonia	*Mansonia altissima*	Africa	High class joinery and furniture
Maple	*Acer* spp.	North America	Flooring, musical instruments
Mashonate /Guariuba	*Clarisia racemosa*	South America	Construction, furniture, mouldings, flooring, turnery
Medang	*Litsea* spp.	South-east Asia	Joinery, carving, furniture, light construction, veneer
Mengkulang	*Heriteria* spp.	South-east Asia	Interior joinery
Meranti / Seraya (parts of Malaysia) and Lauan (Philippines) Red, Yellow and White	*Shorea* spp.	South-east Asia	All types of joinery, framing, doors and fittings. Also used in plywood
Merbau	*Intsia bijuga*	Asia, Africa, Australia, Pacific (main source of timber is Indonesia, Malaysia)	Top quality exterior joinery

Key to threat status CR – Critically Endangered EN – Endangered VU – Vulnerable LR (nt) – Lower Risk

Level of use in the UK	Global threat status	Available as reclaimed?
Minor	VU	
Minor	–	
Minor	–	
Minor	*G. officinale* EN *G. sanctum*: EN Both CITES Appdx II	
Minor	Several species are VU	
Minor	–	Regularly, as antique carving
Minor	–	
Minor	Several species VU	
Major	VU	Regularly, as woodblock flooring
Major	VU, CITES Appdx III (populations in several countries)	Regularly, as woodblock flooring, occasionally as beams
Minor	–	
Minor	EN	
Minor	EN	
Minor	–	Regularly, as wood strip or woodblock flooring
Minor	–	
Minor	*L. leytensis* VU	
Minor	–	
Major	Many *Shorea* species in international trade are CR, EN or VU	Regularly, as woodblock and wood strip flooring, occasionally as beams
Minor	VU	Occasionally as wood strip flooring

Common name	Scientific name	Origin	Uses
Mersawa	*Anisoptera* spp.	South-east Asia	Light construction, furniture, plywood, veneer, marine construction
Mora	*Mora* spp.	South America	Industrial flooring, marine and heavy construction
Muhimbi	*Cynometra alexandri*	Africa	Construction, turnery
Muhuhu	*Brachylaena hutchinsii*	East Africa	High quality flooring subject to heavy wear
Muninga	*Pterocarpus angolensis*	Africa	Panelling and joinery
Mutenye	*Guibourtia arnoldiana*	Africa	Turnery, flooring, furniture, veneer
Niangon	*Heritiera utilis*	West Africa	Furniture
Niove	*Staudtia stipitata*	Africa	Cabinet work, joinery, decorative veneers, flooring, turnery
Nyatoh	*Palaquium* spp.	South-east Asia	Exterior construction, fine furniture, veneer, musical instruments
Oak	*Quercus* spp.	UK, Europe, North America	Wide variety of applications, including joinery, furniture, fittings, flooring
Oak, Tasmanian	*Eucalyptus delegatensis*	Australia	General purpose timber, flooring
Odoko	*Scottellia coriacea*	Africa	Interior and exterior construction, furniture
Ogea	*Daniellia* spp.	Africa	Plywood, joinery, furniture, veneer
Okoume	*Aucoumea klaineana*	Gabon	Plywood
Okwen	*Brachystegia* spp.	Africa	Flooring, veneer, general construction, joinery
Olon	*Fagara heitzii*	Africa	Interior construction, furniture, veneers
Opepe/ Kussia	*Nauclea diderrichii*	West Africa	Outdoor construction, marine defence, sleepers, flooring.
Padauk	*Pterocarpus* spp.	India, Myanmar, West Africa	Joinery, flooring, boat-building
Panga Panga	*Millettia stuhlmanii*	Africa	Cabinet work, joinery, veneer, flooring, turnery, musical instruments
Pau Marfim	*Balfourodendron riedelianum*	Brazil	Furniture making, flooring, construction, turnery
Pear	*Pyrus communis*	Europe	Turnery, carving, drawing instruments, veneer
Peroba Rosa	*Aspidosperma* spp.	South America	Fine furniture, veneer, cabinet work, flooring, interior trim and turning
Persimmon	*Diospyros virginiana*	North America	Decorative ware, musical instruments, turnery

Key to threat status CR – Critically Endangered EN – Endangered VU – Vulnerable LR (nt) – Lower Risk

Level of use in the UK	Global threat status	Available as reclaimed?
Minor	many species CR, EN	
Minor	–	
Minor	–	Occasionally, as woodblock flooring
Minor	–	Regularly, as wood strip and woodblock flooring
Minor	LR (nt)	Regularly, as wood strip and woodblock flooring
Minor	–	
Minor	VU	
Minor	–	
Minor	Several species are VU	
Major	–	Regularly, as reclaimed beams, floorboards, wood strip and woodblock flooring
Minor	–	
Minor	–	
Minor	*D. klainei* LR (nt) *D. oblonga* VU	
Minor	VU	
Minor	*B. kennedyi* VU *B. zenkeri* VU	
Minor	–	
Minor	VU	Occasionally, as beams, woodblock flooring
Minor	*P. indicus* VU	Regularly, as wood strip and woodblock flooring
Minor	–	Regularly, as woodblock flooring
Minor	EN	
Minor	–	
Minor	*A. polyneuron* EN	
Minor	–	

Common name	Scientific name	Origin	Uses
Pine (softwood) various types, also known as Redwood	*Pinus* spp.	UK, Europe (commonly in plantations), North America	General utility work
Pine, Parana (softwood)	*Araucaria angustifolia*	Brazil (some plantations)	Joinery, plywood
Pitch Pine (softwood)	*Pinus* spp.	Southern USA, Brazil (plantations)	Construction, plywood
Plane, European	*Platanus hybrida*	Europe	Veneer, general purpose handles
Poplar	*Populus* spp.	UK, Europe	Matches, turnery, minor craft goods
Purpleheart	*Peltogyne* spp.	Central and South America	Heavy construction work, decorative purposes
Quaruba	*Vochysia* spp.	South America	Carpentry, utility plywood, furniture components, interior trim, millwork
Ramin	*Gonystylus bancanus*	Malaysia, Indonesia	Mouldings
Rauli	*Nothofagus procera*	South America	Furniture, joinery, mouldings, turnery
Rosewood	*Dalbergia* spp.	Africa, South America, India	Furniture, musical instruments
Rubberwood	*Hevea brasiliensis*	Malaysia (plantations)	Furniture
Sapele	*Entandophragma cylindricum*	West Africa	Furniture, joinery, decorative applications
Sepetir	*Sindora* spp.	South-east Asia	Furniture, veneer, light construction, household utensils, plywood, flooring
Sequioa, red	*Sequioa sempervirens*	North America	Joinery
Simpoh	*Dillenia* spp.	South-east Asia	Plywood, interior joinery, furniture and cabinet work
Spruce (softwood), also known as Whitewood	*Picea* spp.	UK, Europe (commonly in plantations), North America	General purpose timber
Sterculia, red	*Sterculia rhinopetala*	Africa	Light construction work, interior joinery, boxes and crates
Swamp sepetir	*Pseudosindora palustris*	South-east Asia	Furniture, cabinet work, joinery, flooring, plywood, veneers

Key to threat status CR – Critically Endangered EN – Endangered VU – Vulnerable LR (nt) – Lower Risk

Level of use in the UK	Global threat status	Available as reclaimed?
Major	–	Regularly as beams, floorboards, wood strip and woodblock flooring
Minor	VU	
Minor	–	
Minor	–	
Minor	–	
Minor	–	Occasionally, as beams
Minor	–	
Major	VU	
Minor	–	
Minor	Various *Dalbergia* species in international trade are threatened *D. nigra* CITES Appdx I	
Major	–	
Major	VU	
Minor	S. *inermis* VU *S. supa* VU	
Minor	–	
Minor	Several species VU	
Major	–	Regularly, as beams, floorboards, wood strip and woodblock flooring
Minor	–	
Minor	–	

Common name	Scientific name	Origin	Uses
Sycamore	*Acer pseudoplatanus*	Europe	Turnery, veneers
Tali	*Erythrophleum* spp.	Africa	Flooring, heavy construction
Tatajuba	*Bagassa guianensis*	South America	Furniture, flooring, joinery, heavy construction
Taun	*Pometia pinnata*	South-east Asia	General purpose timber
Tchitola	*Oxystigma oxyphyllum*	Africa	General purpose timber, veneer, plywood
Teak	*Tectona grandis*	South-east Asia elsewhere)	High quality furniture, joinery, garden furniture (also in plantations
Teak, Rhodesian	*Baikiaea plurijuga*	Southern Africa	Exterior construction, flooring
Terentang	*Campnosperma brevipetiolata*	South-east Asia	Light general purposes
Tiama / Edinam / Cedu nohor	*Entandrophragma angolense*	Africa	Furniture, joinery, construction, flooring
Tornillo	*Cedrelingua cataeneformis*	South America	General construction, furniture
Tulipwood / American poplar	*Liriodendron tulipifera*	North America	Mouldings, drumsticks
Utile / sipo	*Entandophragma utile*	West Africa (Ghana, Cote d'Ivoire)	Furniture, fitments, joinery, construction
Virola	*Virola* spp.	South America	Plywood, mouldings, interior joinery
Vitex	*Vitex confassus*	South-east Asia	Boxes and crates, utility furniture, joinery
Wallaba	*Eperua falcata*	South America	Heavy construction, poles, industrial flooring
Walnut, African /dibetou	*Lovoa trichilioides*	West and Central Africa	Furniture and panelling
Walnut	*Juglans* spp.	Europe, North America	Furniture, joinery, gun butts
Walnut, Queensland	*Endiandra palmerstonii*	Australia	Furniture, interior joinery and construction, veneers
Wawa / Samba / Obeche / Ayous	*Triplochiton scleroxylon*	Africa	Kitchen furniture, mouldings, hidden work, plywood
Wenge	*Millettia laurentii*	Central Africa	Furniture, decorative veneers, speciality uses
Willow	*Salix* spp.	UK, Europe	Cricket bats, basket work, toys and other items
Yew (softwood)	*Taxus baccata*	UK, Europe	Decorative veneer

Key to threat status CR – Critically Endangered EN – Endangered VU – Vulnerable LR (nt) – Lower risk

Level of use in the UK	Global threat status	Available as reclaimed?
Major	–	
Minor	–	
Minor	–	
Minor	–	
Minor	–	
Major	–	Regularly, as wood strip and woodblock flooring, occasionally as beams
Minor	LR (nt)	Regularly, as wood strip and woodblock flooring
Minor	–	
Minor	VU	
Minor	–	
Minor	–	
Major	VU	Regularly, as wood strip and woodblock flooring
Minor	*V. surinamensis* EN	
Minor	–	
Minor	–	
Minor	VU	
Minor		Regularly, as antique panelling and veneered doors
Minor	–	
Major	–	
Minor	EN	Regularly, as woodblock flooring
Minor	–	
Minor	–	

Chapter 7 Listings

The Salvo Code

The Salvo Code is a voluntary code self-policed by dealers, not a legally enforceable Code of Practice. Salvo does not vouch for Salvo Code dealers nor their stock but simply wishes to encourage sensible working practices.

Each Salvo Code dealer undertakes:

- Not to buy any item if there is the slightest suspicion that it is stolen.
- Not to knowingly buy any item removed from listed buildings without listed building consent or from sites of scheduled monuments without scheduled monument consent.
- To record the registration numbers of vehicles belonging to persons unknown who offer items for sale, regardless of whether a purchase is made.
- Where possible to keep a record of the provenance of an item, including the date of manufacture, where it was removed from, and any previous owners.
- To allow their business details to be held on a list of businesses who subscribe to the Salvo Dealer's Code.
- To allow a copy of this Code to be displayed in a public position within their premises.
- To the best of its ability and knowledge to sell material free from toxic chemicals, excepting those natural to the material, traditional to its historical use, or resulting from atmospheric pollution.

Reclaimed timber dealers

This section has been compiled by Salvo, the reclaimed building materials experts, and includes dealers' listings from around the UK. The list consists of companies that deal in reclaimed timber or timber items that would otherwise go to waste; all have signed the voluntary Salvo Code (see left). There are many other dealers in the UK that have not signed the Code; a full regional list can be found in *The Salvo Pack* (price £5.75, available from Salvo), or look on Salvo's web page www.salvo.co.uk (see p82 for Salvo's contact details).

A listing in The *Good wood guide* provides no guarantee of the reputability of the dealer, the quality of the merchandise, or any claims about the environmental properties of the materials sold. Some dealers also sell new timber, in which case, the same criteria apply as with new timber from any other source (i.e. try to buy only FSC-certified wood).

Other local sources of reclaimed, antique or scrap wood:

- friends and neighbours
- skips and local council recycling yards, but ask before you take anything. Taking things out of skips without permission is illegal
- postcards in newsagents windows
- local free newspapers (wants and offers)
- phone books, Yellow Pages under 'demolition' or 'architectural antiques'
- scrap yards
- SalvoWeb DIY Wants & Offers: www.salvoweb.com, or try on-line auctions such as www.iem-net.co.uk (includes building supplies, reclaimed flooring etc).

London

East London

LASSCO
St Michael's Church, Mark Street,
off Paul Street, London EC2A 4ER
Tel: 020 7749 9944   Fax: 020 7749 9941
Email: st.michael@lassco.co.uk
Web: www.lassco.co.uk
Architectural antiques and salvage.
Open: Mon to Sun

Westland & Company
St Michael's Church, Mark Street,
London EC2A 4ER
Tel: 020 7739 8094   Fax: 020 7729 3620
Email: westland@westland.co.uk
Web: www.westland.co.uk
Antique chimneypieces, fine grates, architectural elements, panelling, paintings & furniture
Open: Mon to Sun

North London

LASSCO trade warehouse and LASSCO R.B.K.
101 to 108 Britannia Walk, Islington,
London N1 7LU
Tel: 020 7490 1000   Fax: 020 7490 0908
Email: warehouse@lassco.co.uk
Web: www.lassco.co.uk
Doors, entranceways, woodwork, pub, bygones, metalwork, panelling, lighting, architectural salvage. Trade and overseas buyers welcome. Also old radiators, antique bathrooms, kitchens & kitchenalia, allied salvage
Open: Mon to Sat

North West London

Brondesbury Architectural Reclamation
The Yard, 136 Willesden Lane, Kilburn,
London NW6 7TE
Tel: 020 7328 0820   Fax: 020 7328 0280
Email: mike.carroll@compeer.co.uk
Web: www.brondesburyarchitectural.com
Architectural antiques from Georgian to Edwardian periods, doors, baths, fireplaces, old radiators (& heat output sheets).
Open: Mon to Sun

Retrouvius Reclamation & Design
The Warehouse, 2A Ravensworth Road,
Kensal Green, London NW10 5NR
Tel: 020 8960 6060   Fax: 020 8960 6060
Email: mail@retrouvius.com
Web: www.retrouvius.com
Bridging the gap between construction and destruction; dismantled building components for reuse in interiors & exteriors. (Warehouse open by appointment)

South East London

Ark Architectural Salvage
(formerly Original doors save a tree)
93 Endwell Road, Brockley, London SE4 2NF
Tel: 020 7252 8109
Web: www.salvoweb.com/dealers/ark
Doors, reclaimed kitchens, wardrobes, architectural, doors – DIY or fitted. Things made from reclaimed pine. Plus fireplaces, glass, decorators items
Open: Mon to Sat, Sun am

LASSCo Flooring
41 Maltby Street, Bermondsey,
London SE1 3PA
Tel: 020 7237 4488   Fax: 020 7237 2564
Email: flooring@lassco.co.uk
Web: www.lassco.co.uk
Antique flooring warehouse, contractors, dealers, importers, old oak, Victorian pine, parquet, strip, block, flags, tiles
Open: Mon to Sat

South West London

Crowther of Syon Lodge Ltd
77-79 Pimlico Road, Pimlico,
London SW1 8PH
Tel: 020 7730 8668   Fax: 020 7730 3005
Email: sales@crowthersyonlodge.com
Web: www.crowthersyonlodge.com
Antique garden ornaments, urns, fountains, interior and exterior statuary, antique chimneypieces, old panelled rooms and authentic hand-carved replicas, blacksmith, marble masons and joinery workshops

Nicholas Gifford-Mead Antiques
68 Pimlico Road, London SW1Y 8LS
Tel: 020 7730 6233   Fax: 020 7730 6239
Email: 113046.605@compuserve.com
Fine 18thC and 19thC chimneypieces and garden sculpture; fireplaces
Open: Mon to Fri

Central England

Northamptonshire

Ransford Bros
Drayton Way, Drayton Fields, Daventry,
Northamptonshire NN11 5XW
Tel: 01327 705310   Fax: 01327 706831
Email: enquiries@ransfords.com
Web: www.ransfords.com
Reclaimed bricks, slates, tiles, ridge, coping, setts, railway sleepers, stone, quarries, oak beams, chimney pots, doors, floorboards and new flagstones
Open: Mon to Fri, Sat am

Rococo Antiques & Interiors
5 New Street, Lower Weedon, Weedon Bec,
Northamptonshire NN7 4QS
Tel: 01327 342606
Email: nevillegriffiths@talk21.com
Web: www.nevillegriffiths.co.uk
Also known as Neville's Architectural Salvage Yard. Antique fireplaces, bathrooms, ironwork, reclaimed materials and decorative items
Open: Mon to Sun

Oxfordshire

Oxford Architectural Antiques
16-18 London Street, Faringdon,
Oxfordshire SN7 7AA
Tel: 01367 242268 Fax: 01367 242268
Email: michael@oxfordarchitectural.co.uk
Web: www.oxfordarchitectural.co.uk
Fireplaces, doors, sanitaryware, garden furniture & ornaments, windows, radiators, pine, repro ironware
Open: Tue to Sun

Shropshire

North Shropshire Reclamation & Antique Salvage
Wackley Lodge Farm, Wackley, Burlton,
Shrewsbury, Shropshire SY4 5TD
Tel: 01939 270719 Fax: 01939 270895
Email: enquiries@old2new.uk.com
Web: www.old2new.uk.com
Reclaimed bricks, beams, stone, pavers, bathroom fittings, fireplaces, garden ornaments, troughs, floorboards
Open: Mon to Sun

Priors Reclamation
Unit 2A, Ditton Priors Ind. Estate, Ditton Priors,
Shropshire WV16 6SS
Tel: 01746 712450 Fax: 01746 712450
Email: vicki@priorsrec.co.uk
Web: www.priorsrec.co.uk
Reclaimed wood flooring specialists, stripped pine doors and doors to order, garden antiques
Open: by appointment

Warwickshire

Thomas Crapper & Co Ltd
The Stable Yard, Alscot Park, Stratford On
Avon CV37 8BL
Tel: 01789 450522 Fax: 01789 450523
Email: wc@thomas-crapper.co.uk
Web: www.thomascrapper.co.uk
Makers of Victorian-style sanitaryware, also stocks high quality antique sanitaryware, including wooden toilet seats.
Open: Mon to Sat, by appointment

West Midlands

Coventry Demolition Co
Unit M, Wolston Business Park, Main Street,
Wolston, Coventry, West Midlands CV8 3LL
Tel: 024 7654 5051 Fax: 024 7654 4068
Large stocks of bricks, tiles & slates, doors, oak, paving, cobbles, radiators, fireplaces, timber flooring
Open: Mon to Sat 8 am-5 pm

MDS Ltd
Unit 14, Stechford Trading Estate, Lyndon
Road, Stechford, Birmingham, West Midlands
B33 8BU
Tel: 0121 783 9274 Fax: 0121 783 9274
Web: www.salvoweb.com/dealers/ronnie-wootton
Doors made from reclaimed wood, reclaimed flooring, door furniture and architectural antiques

RBS Oak
Lower Farm, Brandon Lane, Nr Brandon,
Coventry, West Midlands CV3 3GW
Tel: 024 7663 9338 Fax: 01788 540294
Email: rbs@btinternet.com
Web: www.rbsoak.co.uk
Reclaimed timber & oak, also bricks, tiles, slates, flags, quarry tiles, flooring, fireplaces, ironwork
Open: Mon to Sat

Eastern England

Cambridgeshire

The Outback Trading Company
The Architectural Warehouse, Randalls Farm,
Barway, Nr Ely, Cambridgeshire CB7 5UB
Tel: 01353 722560 Fax: 01353 722519
Reclaimed bricks, slates, tiles, oak beams, setts, railway sleepers, flagstones, pub and leisure furniture
Open: Mon to Fri

Solopark plc
Station Road, Nr Pampisford,
Cambridgeshire CB2 4HB
Tel: 01223 834663 Fax: 01223 834780
Email: info@solopark.co.uk
Web: www.solopark.co.uk
Major suppliers of reclaimed building materials, bricks, clay roof tiles, & period architectural antiques, garden antiques, and reproductions; dismantling, reclamation and demolition contractors
Open: Mon to Sat, Sun am

Essex

Ashwell Recycling Co Ltd
Wick Place, Brentwood Road, Bulphan,
Upminster, Essex RM14 3TL
Tel: 01375 892576 Fax: 01375 892330
Secondhand timber, hardwood & softwood, flooring, T&G, beams up to 12in x 12in, plus railway sleepers.
Open: Mon to Fri

Victorian Wood Works Ltd
Creekmouth, 54 River Road,
Barking, Essex IG11 0DW
Tel: 020 8534 1000 Fax: 020 8534 2000
Email: vww@victorianwoodworks.co.uk
Web: www.victorianwoodworks.co.uk
Huge stocks of old oak & pitch pine planks, T & G strip & woodblock. Full installation & floor renovation service
Open: Mon to Fri, Sat am

Norfolk

Mongers
15 Market Place, Hingham, Norwich,
Norfolk NR9 4AF
Tel: 01953 851868 Fax: 01953 851870
Email: mongers@ukgateway.net
Architectural antiques, old bathroom fittings, reclaimed timber & decorative items, old cast iron radiators
Open: Mon to Sat

Suffolk

Abbots Bridge Reclamation Ltd
Lawshall, Bury St Edmunds,
Suffolk IP29 4PB
Tel: 01284 830405 Fax: 01284 830405
Email: enquiries@abbotsbridge.com
Web: www.abbotsbridge.com
Architectural antiques, oak beams, garden antiques, reclaimed building materials, timber flooring (old and new)
Open: By appointment

Heritage Reclamations
1a High Street, Sproughton, Ipswich,
Suffolk IP8 3AF
Tel: 01473 748519 Fax: 01473 748519
Web: www.salvoweb.com/dealers/heritage-reclamation/
Ironmongery, stained glass, lighting, sanitaryware, butler sinks, garden features, flooring, stoves, fireplaces, doors, radiators, furniture
Open: Mon – Fri 9 am to 5 pm, Sat 9.30 am to 5 pm, Sun 10 am to 4 pm

Tower Materials
Tower Farm, Norwich Road,
Mendlesham, Suffolk IP14 5NE
Tel: 01449 766095
Antique oak & elm beams, complete oak framed barns, ironwork, bricks, clay floor tiles. Also known as Preservation in Action.
Open: Anytime by appointment

North West England

Cheshire

Cheshire Demolition & Excavation Contractors Ltd
Moss House, Rear of 72 Moss Lane,
Macclesfield, Cheshire SK11 7TT
Tel: 01625 424433 Fax: 01625 611094
Email:sales@cheshiredemolition.co.uk
Web: www.cheshiredemolition.co.uk
Reclaimed stone, bricks, slates, tiles, oak and pine beams, doors, fireplaces, gateposts, coping and architectural items

Nostalgia
Hollands Mill, 61 Shaw Heath,
Stockport, Cheshire SK3 8BH
Tel: 0161 477 7706 Fax: 0161 477 2267
Email: info@nostalgiafireplaces.co.uk
Web: www.nostalgiafireplaces.co.uk
Over 1400 reclaimed fireplaces of all descriptions, marble chimneypieces a speciality. 200 plus pieces of antique sanitaryware
Open: Tue to Fri 10 am to 6 pm,
Sat 10 am to 5 pm

R & R Renovations & Reclamation
Canalside Yard, Audlem, Cheshire CW3 0DY
Tel: 01270 811310 Fax: 01270 812466
Web: www.salvoweb.com/dealers/rr
Reclaimed bricks, stone, oak beams, tiles, slates, oak barn frames, architectural antiques, bathrooms; dismantling contractors; brick buildings sought
Open: Mon to Fri, Sat am

Greater Manchester

In-Situ Manchester
Talbot Mill, Ellesmere Street, Hulme,
Manchester M15 4JY
Tel: 0161 839 5525
Email: enquiries@insitumanchester.com
Web: www.insitumanchester.com
Buy, restore & sell fireplaces, doors, cast iron, glass, gardenware, flooring.
Open: Mon to Sat

In-Situ Manchester South
149-151 Barton Road, Stretford,
Manchester M32 8DN
Tel: 0161 865 2110
Fireplaces, stoves, radiators, baths, doors, flooring, lighting, glass, furniture & statuary
Open: Mon – Sat 9 am to 5.30 pm
Sun 10 am to 4 pm

Pine Supplies
Lower Tongs Farm, Smithills, Bolton,
Greater Manchester BL1 7PP
Tel: 01204 841416 Fax: 01204 845814
Reclaimed timber merchants, re-sawing and re-machining mouldings, cutting orders fulfilled.

Lancashire

Ribble Reclamation
The Brick House, Ducie Place, off New Hall Lane, Preston, Lancashire PR1 4UJ
Tel: 01772 794534 Fax: 01772 794604
Email: joe@ribble-reclamation.com
Web: www.ribble-reclamation.com/
Antique architectural items for garden and building design, flags, setts, stone, gates, lamp posts, chimneypieces, statuary, troughs, oak beams
Open: Mon to Fri, Sat am

West Yorkshire

Andy Thornton Architectural Antiques Ltd
Victoria Mills, Stainland Road, Greetland,
Halifax, West Yorkshire HX4 8AD
Tel: 01422 377314 Fax: 01422 310372
Email: email@ataa.co.uk
Web: www.andythorntonltd.co.uk
Britain's largest stock of architectural antiques & decor, church interiors, panelled rooms, repro garden ornaments & sculpture, hotel, pub & restaurant refurbishments
Open: Mon to Sun

Bingley Antiques
Springfield Farm Estate, Flappit, Haworth,
West Yorkshire BD21 5PT
Tel: 01535 646666 Fax: 01535 646666
Email: john@bingley-antiques.co.uk
Web: www.bingley-antiques.co.uk
Architectural antiques, leaded glass windows, chimneypots, ironwork, stonework, garden furniture & troughs. Photos of stock can be sent same day by email
Open: Mon to Sat

North East England

Northumberland

Borders Architectural Antiques
2 South Road, Wooler, Northumberland
NE71 6SN
Tel: 01668 282475 Fax: 01668 282475
Web: www.borders-architectural.com
Architectural & garden antiques, stripping, fireplaces, doors, some timber beams and flooring
Open: Phone first

South West England

Bristol

Au Temps Perdu
28-30 Midland Road, St. Phillips,
Bristol BS5 0JY
Tel: 0117 929 9143 or 955 5223
Email: mail@autempsperdu.com
Web: www.autempsperdu.com
Down-to-earth materials at down-to-earth prices. Architectural antiques, reclaimed building materials & restoration
Open: Phone for details

Chaunceys Architectural Antiques
16 Feeder Road, Bristol BS2 0SB
Tel: 0117 971 3131 Fax: 0117 971 2224
Email: sales@chauncey.co.uk
Web: www.chauncey.co.uk
Reclaimed flooring
Open: Mon to Sat

Robert Mills Ltd
Narroways Road, Eastville, Bristol BS2 9XB
Tel: 0117 955 6542 Fax: 0117 955 8146
Email: colin@rmills.co.uk
Web: www.rmills.co.uk
Spectacular architectural antiques for pubs & restaurants, panelling, stained glass, church fittings, reredos, pulpits, prie-dieu and other religious artefacts

Olliff's Architectural Antiques
21 Lower Redland Road, Redland,
Bristol BS6 6JB
Tel: 0117 923 9232 Fax: 0117 923 9880
Email: marcus@olliffs.com
Web: www.olliffs.com
Trader in all types of antique architectural components, garden ornaments, gazebos & summerhouses

Devon

Antique Baths of Ivybridge
Erme Bridge Works, Erme Road,
Ivybridge, Devon PL21 9DD
Tel: 01752 698250 Fax: 01752 698266
Email: antiquebaths@btinternet.com
Web: www.antiquebaths.com
Antique bathroom equipment bought and sold, including wooden toilet seats. Full bath re-enamelling service, in-situ or in workshop.

Tobys
Station House, Station Road, Exminster,
Exeter, Devon, EX6 8DZ
Tel: 01392 833499
Email: paul@tobys-antiques.freeserve.co.uk
Web: www.tobysreclamation.co.uk
Architectural antiques & reclaimed building materials. Antiques, garden statuary, unusual gifts, pine, hardwood, slate & stone flooring, period sanitaryware, original fireplaces, windows, doors & much more. Also at: Newton Abbot & Torquay
Open: Mon to Sat

Dorset

Ace Demolition & Salvage
The Reclamation Centre, Barrack Road,
West Parley, Wimbourne, Dorset BH22 8UB
Tel: 01202 579222 or 580007
Fax: 01202 582043
Email: enquiries@acedemo.co.uk
Web: www.acedemo.co.uk
Reclaimed materials, timber, bricks, tiles, RSJs, slates, architectural items, recycled concrete, sleepers, telegraph poles; demolition and dismantling contractors
Open: Mon to Sat

Dorset Reclamation
The Reclamation Yard, Cow Drove, Bere
Regis, Wareham, Dorset BH20 7JZ
Tel: 01929 472200 Fax: 01929 472292
Email: info@dorsetrec.u-net.com
Web: www.dorsetrec.u-net.com
Reclaimed traditional building materials cleaned & palleted. Architectural antiques & bathroom showrooms
Open: Mon to Sat

Gloucestershire

Architectural Heritage Ltd
Taddington Manor, Taddington, Nr Cutsdean,
Cheltenham, Gloucestershire GL54 5RY
Tel: 01386 584414 Fax: 01386 584236
Email: puddy@architectural-heritage.co.uk
Web: www.architectural-heritage.co.uk
Purveyors of architectural antiques & garden statuary
Open: Mon to Sat

Cox's Architectural Salvage Yard
10 Fosseway Business Park, Moreton in
Marsh, Gloucestershire GL56 9NQ
Tel: 01608 652505 Fax: 01608 652881
Email: coxs@fsbdial.co.uk
Web: www.salvoweb.com/dealers/coxs-architectural
Reclaimed beams, flooring, timber, doors, bathrooms, fire surrounds, fittings, brassware & decorative items.
Open: Mon to Sat

Minchinhampton Architectural Salvage
New Catbrain, Cirencester Road, Aston
Down, Nr Minchinhampton,
Gloucestershire GL6 8PE
Tel: 01285 760886 Fax: 01452 813634
Email: info@catbrain.com
Web: www.catbrain.com
Architectural salvage, garden ornaments, fountains, fireplaces, flooring, timber, railings & gates, baths, bricks, quarries, pavers, slates & tiles
Open: Mon to Fri, Sat & Sun am

The Original Architectural Antiques Co
Ermin Farm, Cirencester,
Gloucestershire GL7 5PN
Tel: 01285 869222 Fax: 01285 868221
Email: sales@ortc.co.uk
Web: www.originaluk.com
Dealers in period and reproduction fireplaces, beams, flooring, troughs, sundials, statuary, gates, urns, doors and quality items of all description
Open: seven days

Somerset

Bridgwater Reclamation Ltd
The Old Co-op Dairy, Monmouth Street,
Bridgwater, Somerset TA6 5EJ
Tel: 01278 424636 Fax: 01278 453666
Dismantling contractors, recycled building materials, Bridgwater Clay roof tile specialist, doors, fireplaces.
Open: Mon to Fri: Sat am

Source
93-95 Walcot Street, Bath,
Somerset BA1 3SD
Tel: 01225 469200
Email: shop@source_antiques.co.uk
Web: www.source-antiques.co.uk
Decorative and architectural antiques, from old to retro, including 1950s items, English Rose and Paul kitchens, revolving summerhouse
Open: Tue to Sat

South West Reclamation
Gwilliams Yard, Edington,
Nr Bridgwater, Somerset TA7 9JN
Tel: 01278 723173 Fax: 01278 722800
Web: www.southwest-rec.co.uk
Reclamation yard specialising in roofing & flooring materials
Open: Mon to Fri, Sat am

Buckinghamshire

Site 77
College Road Business Park, Aston Clinton, Nr Aylesbury, Buckinghamshire HP22 5EZ
Tel: 01296 631717 Fax: 01296 631717
Email: mike@site77.com
Web: www.site77.com
Reclaimed bricks, tiles, slates, oak, doors, York stone, radiators, quarry tiles, setts, flooring etc.
Open: Mon to Sat

IBS Oxford Ltd
Thame Road, Oakley, Buckinghamshire
HP18 9QQ
Tel: 01844 239400 Fax: 01844 239404
Reclaimed materials, old pine, including furniture
Open: Mon to Fri: Sat am

Hampshire

Brook Barn Specialists Ltd
Brook Cottage, Ramsdell, Nr Basingstoke,
Hampshire RG26 5SW
Tel: 0118 981 4379
Large stock top quality oak beams, bricks, tiles, slates, paving
Open: By appointment

Kent

Artisan Oak Buildings Ltd
Teynham Centre, 80 London Road, Teynham
Sittingbourne, Kent ME9 9QH
Tel: 01795 522121 Fax: 01795 520744
Old oak specialists, structural & decorative beams, flooring, cutting, shaping & finishing.
Open: Mon to Sat. Closed Wednesdays.

Catchpole & Rye
Moriartis Workshop, High Halden, Tenterden,
Nr Ashford, Kent TN26 3LY
Tel: 01233 850155 Fax: 01233 850111
Web: www.crye.co.uk
Large stocks of original roll top baths, basins, taps & WC's, including wooden toilet seats. Fine quality bath enamellers. Also reproductions. (Aka 'Posh tubs')
Open: Mon to Sat

Symonds Salvage
Colts Yard, Pluckley Road, Dunsfield,
Bethersden, Nr Ashford, Kent TN26 3DD
Tel: 01233 820724 Fax: 01233 850677
Reclaimed tiles, slates, bricks, oak, doors, windows, stone, garden items, farm tools, furniture & architectural items
Open: Mon to Fri, Sat am

The Architectural Emporium
The Bald Faced Stag, Ashurst, Nr Tunbridge
Wells, Kent TN3 9TE
Tel: 01892 740877
Email: twells@architecturalemporium.com
Web: www.architecturalemporium.com
Garden statuary, lighting, chimneypieces, quality architectural fittings
Open: Mon-Sat 10 am to 5.30 pm

Tina Pasco
Waterlock House, Wingham, Canterbury,
Kent CT3 1BH
Tel: 01227 722151 Fax: 01227 722692
Email: tinapasco@tinapasco.com
Web: www.tinapasco.co.uk
Garden antiques, benches, statuary, fountains, cloche, staddle stones, carved stone remnants, garden tools
Open: seven days

Surrey

Antique Buildings Ltd
Dunsfold, Nr Godalming, Surrey GU8 4NP
Tel: 01483 200477 Fax: 01483 200752
Email: info@antiquebuildings.com
Web: www.antiquebuildings.com
Immense stocks of ancient oak beams, peg tiles, bricks, dismantled barn frames etc.
Open: By appointment

Chancellors Church Furnishings
Rivernook Farm, Sunnyside,
Walton-On-Thames, Surrey KT12 2ET
Tel: 01923 252736 Fax: 01923 252736
Email: info@churchantiques.com
Web: www.churchantiques.com
Architectural antiques and furniture from churches

Comley Lumber Centre
70 Wrecclesham Hill, Farnham,
Surrey GU10 9JX
Tel: 01252 716882 Fax: 01252 715201
Email: comley@comleydemo.co.uk
Web: www.comleydemo.co.uk/index.htm
All types of demolition materials arising from own demolition sites, also fencing materials
Open: Mon – Sat 8 am to 5 pm

Drummonds Architectural Antiques Ltd
The Kirkpatrick Buildings, 25 London Road (A3), Hindhead, Surrey GU26 6AB
Tel: 01428 609444 Fax: 01428 609445
Email: info@drummonds-arch.co.uk
Web: www.drummonds-arch.co.uk
Antique garden statuary, decorative items, quality period bathrooms. Bath vitreous enamelling service
Open: Mon to Sun

Pew Corner
Artington Manor Farm, Old Portsmouth Road, Artington, Guildford, Surrey GU3 1LP
Tel: 01483 533337 Fax: 01483 535554
Email: pewcorner@pewcorner.co.uk
Web: www.pewcorner.co.uk
Absolutely everything from the interior of ecclesiastical buildings. Six-acre site. Repro cast iron furniture
Open: Mon to Sat

Sweerts De Landas
Dunsborough Park, Ripley, Woking,
Surrey GU23 6AL
Tel: 01483 225366 Fax: 01483 224525
Email: garden.ornament@lineone.net
Please phone for an appointment to view the antique garden statuary and ornaments in the 18th century gardens

Woodlands Farm Nursery & Reclamation
The Green, Wood Street Village,
Nr Guildford, Surrey GU3 3DU
Tel: 01483 235536 Fax: 01483 235536
Web: www.salvoweb.com/dealers/woodlands-farm
Trees, Xmas trees & country garden antiques, reclaimed flagstones, bricks, stone, sinks, pavers, troughs, gates

West Sussex

Country Oak Sussex Ltd
Little Washbrook Farm, Brighton Road, Hurstpierpoint, West Sussex BN6 9EF
Tel: 01273 833869 Fax: 01273 833869
Oak beams, oak flooring, antique stone and terracotta flooring, chimneypieces, oak doors, staircases & fittings. Please phone first.
Open: Mon to Fri: Sat am

Scotland

Central

Tradstocks
Dunaverig, Ruskie, Thornhill,
Stirlingshire FK8 3QW
Tel: 01786 850400 Fax: 01786 850404
Email: info@tradstocks.co.uk
Web: www.tradstocks.co.uk
Largest stocks of reclaimed stone in Scotland, flagstones, setts, stone steps, coping, slates, bricks, timber, ironwork, staddle stones. Stone processing.
Open: Mon to Sun

Lothian

Edinburgh Architectural Salvage Yard
Unit 6, Couper Street, off Coburg Street, Leith, Edinburgh, Lothian EH6 6HH
Tel: 0131 554 7077 Fax: 0131 554 3070
Email: lizzie@easy-arch-salv.co.uk Web: www.easy-arch-salv.co.uk
Wide range of antique fireplaces, columns, pews, carved stone, Victorian baths, radiators, ranges and more
Open: Mon to Sat

Rep Of Ireland

Dublin

Architectural Classics
5a Gloucester Street South, Dublin 2
Tel: 086 820 7700
Web: www.architecturalclassics.com
Full range of architectural antiques, bathrooms, doors, garden statuary and ornament, some reproductions

Victorian Salvage & Joinery Co Ltd
8 Brackens Lane, Dublin 2
Tel: 087 293 3694
Web: www.victorian-salvage.com
Reclaimed timber, flooring, resawn beams, furniture and kitchens made using reclaimed wood, old cast iron radiators, antique ironwork (also at 46-47 Townsend Street, Dublin 2)

A number of companies in the UK that buy, sell, or use wood or wood products (including paper) have joined the Worldwide Fund for Nature's 95+ Group, and are committed to selling or using timber products certified by a credible independent certification scheme (FSC), as far as this is possible.

FSC certified timber

The number of FSC certified forests is increasing all the time, as is the number of products available and stockists of these products, so any list of forests or products printed here would quickly become obsolete. A number of companies in the UK that buy, sell, or use wood or wood products (including paper) have joined the Worldwide Fund for Nature's 95+ Group, and are thus committed to selling or using timber products certified by a credible independent certification scheme (FSC), as far as this is possible. These companies are therefore a good place to start when trying to find FSC certified timber.

The list of 95+ Group members overleaf, correct as of August 2001, includes companies that are involved in the timber trade or are major timber users (95+ Group members dealing solely in paper products are not included). New companies are still joining the 95+ Group, so for a completely up-to-date list, consult WWF's web-page (www.panda.org/forestandtrade, go to About the Network, then Network Members). Note that not all companies listed, retail to the public.

Readers are also referred to the following websites:

www.fsc-uk.demon.co.uk – FSC-UK's website, with lists of FSC certified timbers and products, and where to buy them.

www.fscoax.org – FSC international's website; documents available include a list of FSC certified forests around the world.

Those without internet access can contact the FSC-UK office on tel: 01686 413916.

95+ Group members dealing in timber and timber products
(head office details for those with multiple locations)

DIY stores and garden products

B&Q Plc
DIY and Garden Centre Superstore
Portswood House, 1 Hampshire
Corporate Park
Chandlers Ford, Hants SO53 3YX
Tel: 023 8025 6256
Fax: 023 8025 7287

E C Walton & Co Ltd
Manufacturers and suppliers of garden buildings
Old Great North Road, Sutton-on-Trent
Newark, Notts NG23 6QN
Tel: 01636 821215
Fax: 01636 822027

Focus Group Limited
(Focus, Focus Do It All, Great Mills, No Frills DIY and Wickes Building Supplies)
DIY and gardening products, timber, building supplies.
Gawsworth House,
Westmere Drive, Crewe, Cheshire CW1 6JD
Tel: 01270 501555
Fax: 01270 250501

Forest Garden plc
Sawmilling home grown and imported timber for garden products
Stanford Court, Stanford Bridge
Nr Worcester WR6 6SR
Tel: 01886 812451 / 01576 205400
Fax: 01886 812343 / 01576 205422

Grange Fencing Limited
Manufacturer of garden fencing, trellises and garden structures
Halesfield 21, Telford, Shropshire TF7 4PA
Tel.: 01952 586460
Fax: 01952 586668

Homebase
DIY retailer
Beddington House
Wallington, Surrey SM6 OHB
Tel: 020 8784 6529
Fax: 020 8784 6849

Magnet Limited
DIY Retailer
Royd Ings Ave., Keighley, W.Yorks BD21 4BY
Tel: 01535 661133
Fax: 01535 691780

Style Gardens
A national e-commerce garden retail business
Port Road, Wenvoe, Cardiff CV5 6AD
Tel: 029 2059 0011
Fax: 029 2059 3888

True Temper Ltd
Suppliers of garden tools
Whites Cross, Cork, Republic of Ireland
Tel: 00 353 21 4302 433
Fax: 00 353 21 4304 621

Timber merchants and building supplies

Beacon Certified Timber
Source and supply service for temperate timbers, and wood products
2A Rutland Square
Edinburgh EH1 2AS
Tel: 0131 228 7575
Fax: 0131 229 4827

C Blumsom Ltd
Hardwood and softwood importers and merchants
Maple Wharf, 36-38 River Road
Barking, Essex IG11 0DN
Tel: 020 8594 5175
Fax: 020 85941089

Clarks Wood Company Ltd
Timber importers
Silverthorn Wharf, Bristol BS2 OQJ
Tel: 0117 971 6316
Fax: 0117 972 3119

Conven Limited
Merchants and importers of wood veneers
Nashlea Farm, Poors Lane North
Thundersley, Essex SS7 2XF
Tel: 01702 554123
Fax: 01702 551184

Eastern Hardwoods Limited
Timber Importer
4 Ash Industrial Estate, Flex Meadow
Pinnacles West, Harlow, Essex CM19 5TJ
Tel: 01279 453582
Fax: 01279 453714

Ecotimber Ltd
Timber agent
6 Salisbury Avenue, Pennarth
Cardiff CF64 3JA
Tel: 029 2070 7444
Fax: 029 2071 1133

Ellis-Hill Limited
Timber importer and merchant
843-855 Leeds Road,
Huddersfield HD2 1WA
Tel: 01484 451338
Fax: 01484 451340

International Timber
Timber Distribution
West Yard, Trafford Wharf Road,
Trafford Park, Manchester M17 1DJ
Tel: 0161 848 2900
Fax: 0161 848 2914

Jewsons Ltd
Builders Merchants
Merchant House
Binley Business Park, Coventry, CV3 2TT
Tel: 024 7643 8400
Fax: 024 7643 8851

Timbmet Limited
Timber Importer
PO Box 39, Chawley Works
Cumnor Hill, Oxford OX2 9PP
Tel: 01865 862223
Fax: 01865 864825

Timber products

Richard Burbidge Limited
Moulded wood products
Whittingdon Road, Oswestry,
Shropshire. SY11 1HZ
Tel: 01691 655131
Fax: 01691 670169

Chindwell Company Limited
Supplier of doors
Hyde House, The Hyde, London NW9 6JT
Tel: 020 8205 6171
Fax: 020 8205 8800

F R Shadbolt & Sons Ltd
Manufacturers of wood panels and doors
Shadbolt Avenue, London E4 8PZ
Tel: 0208 5276441
Fax: 0208 5232774

F W Mason & Sons Ltd
Manufacturers and distributors of solid wood products
Colwick Industrial Estate
Nottingham NG4 2EQ
Tel: 0115 911 3500
Fax: 0115 911 3555

Kronospan Ltd
Wood Panel Manufacturer
Chirk, Wrexham LL14 5NT
Tel: 01691 773361
Fax: 01691 775239

Calders and Grandidge
Specialist Timber Products and timber treatment
194 London Road, Boston
Lincolnshire, PE21 7HJ
Tel: 01205 358866
Fax: 01205 312421

International Decorative Services
Decorative services and panel products
Unit 13 Ponders End Ind Est
35 East Duck Lees Lane
Endsfield, Middlesex EN3 7RD
Tel: 020 8443 3320
Fax: 020 8805 3481

Furniture

Blue Line Office Furniture
Office furniture
Blue Line House, 17-19 Thames Road
Barking, Essex IG11 0HS
Tel: 020 8594 3115
Fax: 020 8591 2639

Core Products Ltd
Importers and distributers of pine shelving and storage units
Unit 3, Arran House, Arran Rd,
Perth PH1 3DZ
Tel: 01738 630555
Fax: 01738 630500

David Craig
Garden Furniture
The Mill, Mill Lane,
Langley Moor, Durham DH7 8JE
Tel: 0191 378 1211
Fax: 0191 378 0411

Doorvale Limited
Manufacture and production of bathroom furniture
Unit A, Portland Industrial Estate
Southwell Lane, Kirby-in-Ashfield
Nottinghamshire NG17 8BZ
Tel: 01623 754605
Fax: 01623 750852

Douglas Kane
Manufacturer and supplier of hardware, cabinet furniture
Rothley House, Erdington Industrial Park
Chester Road, Birmingham B24 0RD
Tel: 0121 377 6077
Fax: 0121 377 6063

Fairwinds Europe Ltd
Furniture designer and manufacturer
Faraday Drive, Stourbridge Road, Bridgnorth
Shropshire WV15 5BA
Tel: 01746 767108
Fax: 01746 767242

Indian Ocean Trading Company Ltd
Outdoor furniture
155-163 Balham Hill, London SW12 9DJ
Tel: 020 8675 4808
Fax: 020 8675 4652

Jacuzzi UK
Bathroom manufacturer
PO Box 155, Woodlands
Euroway Trading Estate, Bradford BD4 6ST
Tel: 01274 654700
Fax: 01274 654730

Moores Furniture Group Ltd
Manufacturer of kitchen, bedroom and bathroom furniture
Queen Mary House,
Thorp Arch Trading Estate
Wetherby, West Yorkshire LS23 7DD
Tel: 01937 844300
Fax: 01937 845439

Newcastle Furniture Company Limited
Custom made furniture
Green Lane Buildings, Pelaw Industrial
Estate, Pelaw, Tyne & Wear NE10 0UW
Tel: 0191 438 1342
Fax: 0191 438 4698

Spur Shelving
Manufacturer of shelving systems
Spur House,Otterspool Way
Watford, Herts WD2 8HT
Tel: 01923 226071
Fax: 01923 238312

The Symphony Group PLC
Manufacturer of kitchen, bedroom and occasional furniture
Geldered Lane, Leeds LS12 6AL
Tel: 0113 230 8000
Fax: 0113 230 8115

Construction and engineering

Balfour Beatty Rail Projects Limited
Design, project management and construction of rail projects
Room 208B, Midland House
Nelson Street, Derby DE1 2SA
Tel: 01332 262816
Fax: 01332 262832

Bovis Lend Lease Ltd
Project management & construction services
142 Northolt Rd, Harrow, Middlesex
HA2 0EE
Tel: 020 8276 2694
Fax: 020 8276 2672

Carillion plc
Construction and civil engineering
Kirkintilloch Road, Bishopbriggs,
Glasgow G64 2PS
Tel: 0141 762 2266
Fax: 0870 128 5308

Laing Homes Limited
House builders
Caspian House, The Waterfront
Elstree Road, Elstree, Herts WD6 3BS
Tel: 020 8236 8799
Fax: 020 8236 8701

Morrison Construction Limited
Construction company
Pictow Farm Road, Runcorn
Cheshire WA7 4UN
Tel: 01928 580780
Fax: 01928 580168

National Railway Supplies Limited
Supplier of railway infrastructure products
Gresty Road, Crewe, Cheshire CW2 6EH
Tel: 01270 533282
Fax: 01270 532121

Charcoal

Bioregional Charcoal Company Limited
Suppliers of British charcoal and firewood
Sutton Ecology Centre, Honeywood Walk,
Carshalton Surrey SM5 3MX
Tel: 020 8669 0713 or 020 8773 2044
Fax: 020 8773 2878

CPL Chartan-Aldred
Manufacturers of charcoal
Lawn Road Industrial Estate
Carlton In Lindrick, Worksop, Notts S81 9LB
Tel: 01909 541200
Fax: 01909 541222

Parlour Products Limited
Charcoal and BBQs
Farndon Business Centre, Farndon Road
Market Harborough, Leics LE16 9NP
Tel: 01858 469800
Fax: 01858 410168

Rectella International Limited
Manufacturer of charcoal
Queensway House
Queensway, Clitheroe, Lancashire BB7 1AU
Tel: 01200 442299
Fax: 01200 452010

Retailers – miscellaneous items

The Body Shop International PLC
Cosmetic suppliers and retailers
Watersmead Littlehampton,
West Sussex BN17 6LS
Tel: 01903 731500
Fax: 01903 844431

Boots The Chemists Ltd
Retail chemists
Product Quality and Development Centre
PO Box 5302, Nottingham NG2 1HB
Tel: 0115 950 6111
Fax: 0115 847 2831

Co-operative Retail
(Part of the Co-operative Group)
Retailer and Wholesaler
4th Floor, Old Bank Building, P.O. Box 53,
New Century House, Manchester M60 4ES
Tel: 0161 827 5074
Fax: 0161 827 5750

Sainsbury's Supermarkets Ltd
Retailers of diverse range of paper, pulp and timber products
Rennie House, Stamford St, London SE1 9LL
Tel: 020 7695 7159
Fax: 020 7695 7790

Tesco Stores Ltd
Supermarket
PO Box 44, Cirrus Building, Shire Park,
Welwyn Garden City, Herts AL7 1ZR
Tel: 01707 297725
Fax: 01707 297797

Manufacturers – miscellaneous items

Charles Bentley & Son
Manufacturer of brushes
Central House
Jubilee Drive, Loughborough LE11 5TP
Tel: 01509 232757
Fax: 01509 233861

Design for Nature Ltd
Bird feeding & breeding products
Unit 5, 19/21 Cornish Way,
North Walsham, Norfolk NR28 0AW
Tel: 01692 409900
Fax: 01692 409901

Fantasia Limited
Global distributor of quality pencils
Andre House, Salisbury Square
Old Hatfield, Herts AL9 5BJ
Tel: 01707 264066
Fax: 01707 262741

H & L Russel Ltd
Housewares importers and distributers
438 Upper Brentwood Road
Gidea Park, Romford, Essex RM2 6JE
Tel: 01708 473111
Fax: 01708 448871

Impress Group Limited
Manufacturer of picture frames
Stafford Park 1, Telford, Shropshire TF3 3BT
Tel: 01952 423303
Fax: 01952 423342

Newell Window Fashions UK
Curtain poles and accessories
Tamworth Site, Mariner
Tamworth, Staffordshire B79 7TW
Tel: 01827 64242
Fax: 01827 205308

Remarkable Pencils Ltd
Manufacturer of pencils and paper products
56 Glentham Road, London SW13 9JJ
Tel: 020 8741 1234
Fax: 020 7352 4729

Shireclose Housewares Ltd
Supplier of domestic kitchen woodware
Shawlands Court, Newchapel Road
Lingfield, Surrey RH7 6BL
Tel: 01342 835800
Fax: 01342 836234

Stanley Tools
Manufacturer of paint brushes, rollers and decorators materials
Hellaby Industrial Estate,
Hellaby Lane, Hellaby
Rotherham S66 8HN
Tel: 0114 276 8888
Fax: 0114 282 2078

T&G Woodware Limited
Suppliers of kitchen woodware
Old Mill Road, Portishead, Bristol BS20 9BX
Tel: 01275 841841
Fax: 01275 841800

Wooden Wonders Ltd
Wooden giftware manufacturer
Farley Farm House
Chiddlingly, East Sussex BN8 6HW
Tel: 01825 872856
Fax: 01825 872733

Forest Management

Scottish Woodlands Ltd
Forest management company, providing services to all sectors of the forest industry
Research Park, Riccarton,
Edinburgh EH14 4AP
Tel: 0131 451 5154
Fax: 0131 451 5146

The Woodland Trust
Woodland management and conservation
Autumn Park, Dysart Road, Grantham,
Lincs NG31 6LL
Tel: 01424 773160
Fax: 01424 773160

Non-wood alternatives

Brooks Manson Ltd
Daleside Road
Nottingham NG2 4DH
Tel: 0115 950 7396
Fax: 0115 958 0728
Email: brooks.nottingham@upm-kymmene.com
Imports strawboard from Germany.

Construction Resources
16 Great Guildford Street
London
SE1 0HS
Tel: 020 7450 2211
Fax: 020 7450 2212
Email: info@ecoconstruct.com
Suppliers of non-wood boards and ecological building materials, including EMFA coconut fibre board, Fermacell (made from recycled gypsum and cellulose) and Clayboard (made from reeds and clay). Also source of advice on ecological building.

William T. Eden
Enterprise Close,
Medway City Estate,
Frindsbury,
Rochester ME2 4LY
Sells flaxboard imported from Belgium.

Chapter 8 Further information sources

Fauna & Flora International
Great Eastern House
Tenison Road
Cambridge
CB1 2TT
Tel: 01223 571000
Web: www.fauna-flora.org
Email: info@fauna-flora.org

Friends of the Earth
26-28 Underwood Street
London
N1 7JQ
Tel: 020 7490 1555
Web: www.foe.co.uk
Email: info@foe.co.uk

SALVO
PO Box 333
Cornhill-on-Tweed
TD12 4YJ
Tel: 01980 820333
Web: www.salvo.co.uk

UNEP – World Conservation Monitoring Centre
219c Huntingdon Road
Cambridge
CB3 0DL
Tel: 01223 277314
Web: www.unep-wcmc.org
Includes the Tree Conservation Information Service (www.unep-wcmc/trees/index.html)

Forest Stewardship Council UK
Unit D
Station Building
Llanidloes
Wales
SY18 6EB
Tel: 01686 413916
Web: www.fsc-uk.demon.co.uk

Association of Environment Conscious Building
PO Box 32
Llandysul
Wales
SA44 5ZA
Tel: 01559 370908
Web: www.aecb.net

Construction Resources
16 Great Guildford Street
London
SE1 0HS
Tel: 020 7450 2211
Fax: 020 7450 2212
Email: info@ecoconstruct.com
Web: www.ecoconstruct.com

SOFA – the Furniture Recycling Network
C/o CFS
The Old Drill Hall
17A Vicarage Street North
Wakefield
WF1 4JS
Tel: 01924 375252
Web: www.btinternet.com/~frn/FRN

Woods of the World
A web-based database hosted by ForestWorld.com, giving technical properties for over 900 timbers
Web: www.forestworld.com – click on Woods of the World
Note: information on FSC certified products on ForestWorld.com does not include all UK retailers – see the FSC website www.fsc-uk.demon.co.uk for a full list.

Selected further reading

There are many publications and websites on forests, the timber industry, wood use etc. The following is a very small selection that are particularly relevant to the issues in this guide. It is by no means comprehensive.

The World List of Threatened Trees. Oldfield, S, Lusty, C and MacKinven, A (1998). World Conservation Press, Cambridge, UK. Available from UNEP-World Conservation Monitoring Centre (see above).

Our Forests, Our Future. Report of the World Commission on Forests and Sustainable Development, (1999). Cambridge University Press, Cambridge, UK.

The Last Frontier Forests. World Resources Institute (1997). Available from World Resources Institute, 1709 New York Avenue NW., Washington, DC 20006, USA. Tel: 00 1 202 729 7600; Fax: 00 1 202 729 7610; Web: www.wri.org/wri

Bad Harvest: the timber trade and the degradation of the world's forests. Dudley, N Jeanrenaud, J P and Sullivan, F (1995). Book published in collaboration with WWF by Earthscan Publications, London.

Behind the Logo: an environmental and social assessment of forest certification schemes. FERN (2001). Report available from FERN, Fosseway Business Centre 1C, Stratford Road, Moreton-in-Marsh, Gloucestershire, GL56 9NQ Tel: 01608 652895 Fax: 01608 652878, www.fern.org (report available online).

Out of the Woods: reducing wood consumption to save the world's forests. A Plan for action in the UK. Friends of the Earth (1995). Report available from Friends of the Earth (see above).

An introduction to wood waste in the UK. Magin, G (2001). Report available from Fauna & Flora International (see above).

What's wrong with PVC? and **Building the Future – a guide to building without PVC**. Reports available from Greenpeace, Canonbury Villas, London N1 2PN; Tel: 020 7865 8100; www.greenpeace.org/~uk

Green Building Handbook (A Guide to Building products and their Environment) Volume 1. Woolley, T, Kimmins, S and Harrison. R (1999) 224pp. ISBN 0-419 22690-7; **Green Building Handbook Volume 2**. Woolley, T. and Kimmins, S. (2000) 192pp. ISBN 0-419-25380-7

Environmental Building News, monthly newsletter produced by BuildingGreen, 122 Birge Street, Suite 30, Brattleboro, USA VT 05301 Tel: 001 802/257 7300; www.buildinggreen.com

Efficient Wood Use in Residential Construction. Natural Resources Defences Council (1998). Excerpts from report available online at www.nrdc.org, or contact Natural Resources Defence Council, 40 West 20th Street, New York, USA, NY 10011 Tel: 00 1 212 727-2700; Fax: 00 1 212 727-1773; Email: nrdcinfo@nrdc.org

The Ecological Building Network. Website with information on efficient and ecological construction. www.ecobuildnetwork.org

European League Table of Imports of Illegal Tropical Timber. Friends of the Earth briefing.

Friends of the Earth

About Friends of the Earth

Friends of the Earth is the UK's most influential national environmental campaigning organisation. With almost one million supporters across five continents and over 60 national organisations worldwide, it is the most extensive environmental network in the world.

Our vision is a world where everyone's needs are met in a way which values our quality of life and safeguards the future of the environment. We campaign to stop the rapid exploitation of the Earth's resources that is polluting the planet and causing growing inequality between rich and poor. Most environmental damage is caused by rich countries, which have a fraction of the world's population. We want to stop this exploitation and ensure that rich countries pay a fair price for what they use.

Friends of the Earth has been campaigning to save the world's forests for 30 years. Campaigns have ranged from the local – saving UK woodlands – to the international – to close down the illegal trade in Brazilian mahogany. As part of its new Corporates Campaign, Friends of the Earth is investigating and exposing the corporations involved in illegal and unsustainable logging. Friends of the Earth is campaigning for new international laws to hold corporations accountable and to eliminate illegal logging. The UK, as one of the world's biggest consumer of timber products, has a huge responsibility for driving the destruction of the world's forests. Friends of the Earth is proud to be involved in the *Good wood guide* which we hope will act as a practical tool for all buyers of timber products to minimise their forest footprint. Time for the world's forests is running out. By taking care to purchase good wood, UK consumers can play an invaluable role in helping to save them.

About Fauna & Flora International

Fauna & Flora International acts to conserve threatened species and ecosystems world-wide, choosing solutions that are sustainable, are based on sound science and take account of human needs. The world's oldest international conservation organisation, Fauna & Flora International is currently supporting over 100 projects in 60 countries.

The Global Trees Campaign

The Global Trees Campaign, developed by Fauna & Flora International and the United Nations Environment Programme-World Conservation Monitoring Centre, aims to save the most threatened tree species and the habitats where they grow through information, conservation and wise use. The Campaign focuses on trees as flagship species for ecosystem and landscape conservation and enables local people to carry out rescue and sustainable use operations. With our support, work to save endangered tree species is currently underway or planned in Belize, Brazil, Chile, Dominica, Ecuador, Liberia, Mexico, Mozambique, Philippines, South Africa, Tanzania and Vietnam. The promotion of sustainable wood use, through waste minimisation and forest certification, are essential components of the Global Trees Campaign. A special programme called SoundWood focuses on the future of trees used to make musical instruments – many such trees are becoming rare or endangered.

About Salvo

Salvo was set up in 1991 to provide information about buying, selling and reusing old materials for buildings and gardens. It networks information to subscribing dealers in Britain and abroad. Salvo publishes a fortnightly newsletter, *SalvoNews*, and a magazine, *SALVO*.

In 1995 Salvo set up the Salvo Code (see page 66), which over 100 dealers have now signed. This simple code aims to give buyers the confidence that items they bought have not been stolen or removed from listed or protected buildings without permission.

Salvo sells *The Salvo Pack* (£5.75 by mail order in UK), which contains a regional directory of suppliers and other useful addresses, a free copy of *SalvoNews* and *SALVO* magazine and a complete list of all Salvo Code dealers. It also provides information about dealers in other countries. For example, *The French Salvo Pack* (£10 mail order) contains regional listings of dealers in France.

Since 1992, Salvo has run a Theft alert system for people whose gardens, or occasionally buildings, have been robbed of antique materials. Salvo also runs a DIY Wants and Offers section on its web page, where individuals with items to sell or who are seeking particular goods or materials can advertise.

Appendix International initiatives to save the forests

There have been many intergovernmental initiatives aimed at addressing the forest crisis. Most have been at best ineffectual and some (eg the Tropical Forestry Action Plan in the 1980s) have been blamed for worsening the problem. It is important that international efforts continue to tackle both the direct causes of the forest crises (including uncontrolled logging), and the complex external issues that impact on forests, such as debt, poverty, land tenure, poor governance, the international trade regime, and the lack of recognition in economic terms of non-monetory forest goods and services (so-called "missing markets"). National efforts are also vital, and some governments, including those in tropical countries, are making serious efforts to tackle the situation nationally. The following are the most recent or on-going intergovernmental initiatives on forests.

*Full title: Non-legally Binding Authoritative Statement of Principles for a Global Consensus on the Management, Conservation and Sustainable Development of all Types of Forest.

The Forest Principles (1992)
The Forest Principles*, a set of non-legally binding principles for sustainable forest management, are the outcome of forest-related discussions at the Rio Earth Summit. Many were hoping for a legally binding convention on forests to emerge from the Earth Summit, but this was not achieved.

Intergovernmental Panel on Forests (IPF) / Intergovernmental Forum on Forests (IFF)
Intergovernmental dialogue continued after Rio under the United Nations umbrella, with the IPF (1995-1997), then the IFF (1997-2000). These failed to produce any real concrete outcomes, although the IPF did agree on a set of Proposals for Action.

United Nations Forum on Forests (UNFF)
A new permanent body created at the end of the IFF, charged with facilitating and monitoring the implementation of the IPF's Proposals for Action.

Convention on Biological Diversity (CBD)
Agreed at the Rio Earth Summit, the CBD is elaborating a programme for forest biodiversity.

Global Forest Convention (not agreed)
One of the issues dominating the post-Rio intergovernmental dialogue on forests has been the desirability or otherwise of a legally binding global forest

convention. Several large timber-producing countries, notably Canada and Malaysia, have lobbied hard for a convention to be set up. But, most environmental NGOs no longer support the idea, believing that it would end up as a "loggers convention", that it would take control of forest resources further away from local people, and that another convention is unlikely to have a major impact but would be extremely expensive in terms of time and resources.

The Convention on the International Trade in Endangered Species of Wild Fauna and Flora (CITES)
CITES is a intergovernmental agreement aimed at regulating the international trade in wildlife. Species can be listed on one of three appendices to the treaty, which impose various levels of restriction on international trade. Although there have been attempts by environmentalists and some governments to list a range of over-exploited timber species on CITES, there are currently just 19 timber trees covered by the agreement, of which only a few are major timbers. Producer countries frequently oppose moves to list species to protect their logging interests, although some appreciate the help it can provide in controlling trade in over-exploited species.

Criteria and Indicators for Sustainable Forest Management
A series of regional intergovernmental processes has resulted in several Criteria and Indicators for Sustainable Forest Management (the Helsinki Process for Europe, the Montreal Process for temperate and boreal forest outside Europe, The Tarapoto process for Amazonian forests, and processes for dry-zone Africa, the Near East region and Central America). These documents are designed to help governments implement and monitor sustainable management in their forests.

The International Tropical Timber Organisation (ITTO)
The ITTO is an intergovernmental organisation formed in 1983 with the aim of providing a framework for consultation among producer and consumer member countries on all aspects of the world timber economy. The ITTO's objective, Target 2000, states that by the year 2000, all tropical timber products traded internationally by Member States should originate from sustainably managed forests. This target is far from being achieved – even the ITTO's own review of progress towards the target published in 2001 states that "*...the journey is just beginning*".

G8 Programme for Forests
In 1997 the G8 nations declared a special programme for forests, which was further elaborated at their 1998 summit in Birmingham. The programme included a call to member governments to take action to combat illegal logging. Within the G8 Programme, the UK government has been designated to take the lead on this issue.